# COMBAT AND SURVIVAL

WHAT IT TAKES TO FIGHT AND WIN

VOLUME

5

Originally published in the United Kingdom in weekly parts **COMBAT & SURVIVAL** is a study of the armed forces at work. It shows the skills taught to soldiers and the way in which military units operate. It examines the weapons and equipment used by different armies; and, by looking at recruit training and exercises, **COMBAT & SURVIVAL** demonstrates how the armed forces develop individual responsibility, leadership and initiative.

# COMBAT AND SURVIVAL

WHAT IT TAKES TO FIGHT AND WIN

VOLUME

5

H. S. STUTTMAN, INC. *publishers* Westport, Connecticut 06889

# Contents

## Volume 5



Published by H. S. STUTTMAN INC.
Westport, Connecticut 06889

ISBN 0-87475-560-3

All individual combat and personal survival activities involve risk or injury, to oneself and others, and great care must be taken in carrying out any such activities. Expert guidance should be sought and equipment checked for reliability before any activities described in this work are carried out. The publishers cannot assume responsibility for damage to property or injury, death or loss to persons which may result from carrying out the activities described in this work. In carrying out any activities described in this work, persons do so entirely at their own risk.

PRINTED IN THE UNITED STATES OF AMERICA

1P(1632)30

# INFANTRY TACTICS IN BUILT-UP AREAS

***Street fighting, especially the difficult and dangerous job of house-clearing, is some of the most nerve-racking work you will ever do as a soldier.*** City streets are deadly places for the attacking soldier. Every doorway and window, every pile of rubble and seemingly abandoned vehicle, every rooftop and underground passage, could contain a fatal hazard for the unwary.

On a city street you can make no assumptions until you've seen, checked and double-checked for yourself; and even then you must expect the unexpected at any moment, day or night.

Your life depends on your alertness, and you must rely on your basic training to see you safely through. This section is based on the US Infantry Fighting Manual. It is the first in a series that looks in detail at all the skills a soldier needs to survive in an urban battle.

## *The tricks of the trade*

The rifle squad is the basic unit for street fighting. Every member of the squad must know all the tricks of his trade: how to move through the streets, how to enter and clear build-

***Before going into the building, the experienced infantryman sends a grenade in ahead to kill, stun or drive out anyone who may be inside.***

## *Seven life-saving rules of movement*

**There are seven basic rules of movement.**

1. **Never allow yourself to be seen in silhouette, and keep low at all times.**
2. **Avoid open spaces.**
3. **Select your next position in cover before you make your move.**
4. **Hide your movements any way you can.**
5. **Move fast.**
6. **Stay clear of covering fire.**
7. **Be alert and ready for anything.**

***Look first, move later. This simple formula has saved the life of many a patrolling foot-soldier.***

*These two infantrymen are working as a team to minimise the danger from enemy forces inside the house, during the American invasion of Grenada in 1983.*

ings, how to use grenades, how to choose firing positions, what camouflage techniques and special weapons (flame-throwers and smoke bombs, for example) to use to best effect.

### Movement

The moment you stop moving, your attack stops too. Then you are at the mercy of the enemy forces who possess the advantage of a secure defensive position. The attacking force must dictate the pace of the battle or lose the initiative.

The important rule is to move as fast as possible to present the smallest target.

### Moving in the open

You should try to move down a street through the buildings on either side by making holes in their internal walls. If you must move in the open, use smoke screens and covering fire at all times. Stay close to the walls, and in the shadows. Keep low, don't present your silhouette and, above all, move fast. This way, it will be very difficult for an enemy gunner inside the building to get a clear shot at you without exposing himself to covering fire from your teammates. Always remember: work as a team. Everyone then stands a better chance of surviving unhurt.

*These US Marines are using what available cover they can in an attempt to take out an enemy sniper during the battle for Hue, South Vietnam, in 1968.*

# Urban movement techniques

***Moving from place to place under fire is always a dangerous business. Movement in towns and cities calls for a different set of skills from those used out in the country, but you must still be alert to every possibility of danger.***

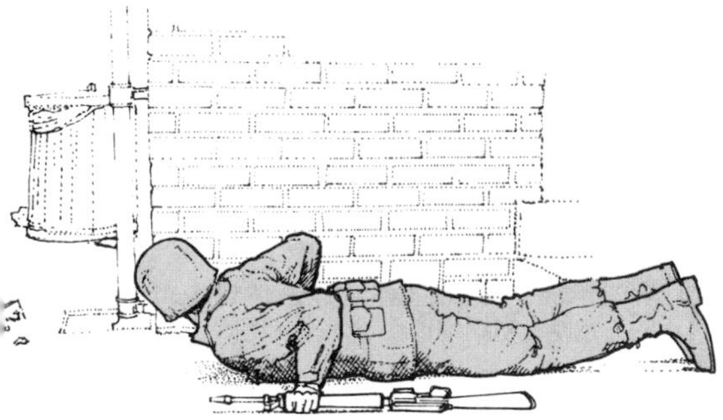

**The lie of the land**
Looking around corners carelessly is a quick way to get killed. Do it at ground level. Always remember to keep your weapon well back out of sight and wear your Kevlar helmet.

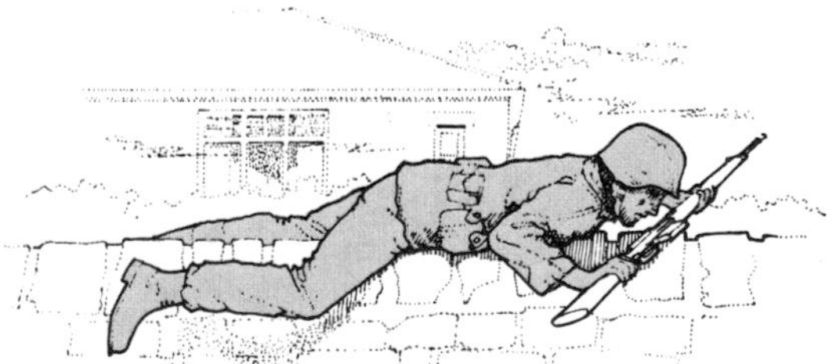

**Over the wall**
When crossing a wall you must keep as low a profile as possible. Roll over it, with your body flat. If you don't know what is on the other side, throw a grenade over first – but be sure that shrapnel splinters can't reach you through the wall.

**Mind your head**
Be careful when you pass by ground floor windows. Always be sure to keep your head well down below the level of the sill.

# Firing positions

***The infantryman looks for two things in a firing position – concealment for himself and his weapon, and a wide field of fire. His assessment of any situation must be second nature.***

**Rooftops and chimneys**
The rooftop is a commanding position, but still you must take care not to silhouette yourself against the skyline. Firing around a chimney will give you extra cover.

**Loose masonry**
Always keep as low as you can, to present the smallest possible target. Loose rubble like this provides excellent cover because of its uneven profile.

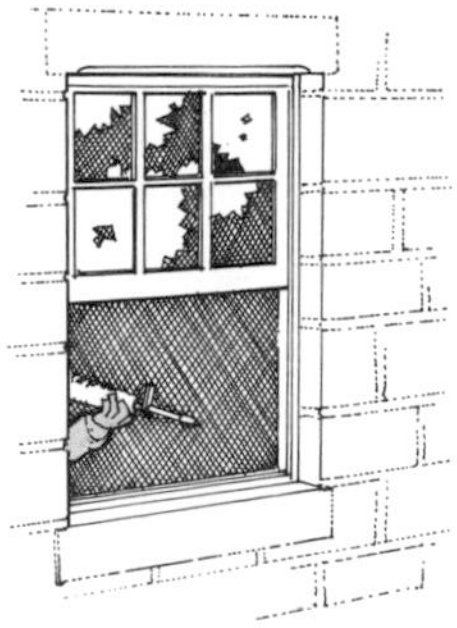

**Windows and loopholes**
Only a fool would get so close to a window as to allow himself to be seen through it. Stay well back in the darkness and safety of the room.

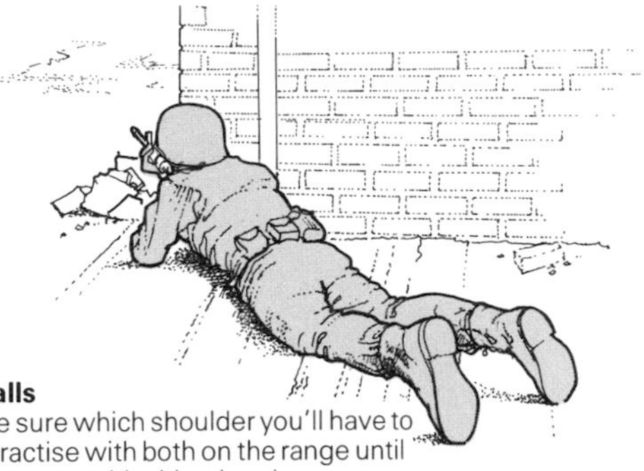

**Corners and walls**
You can never be sure which shoulder you'll have to shoot from, so practise with both on the range until you're equally accurate with either hand.

**Muzzle flash**
Even though modern weapons are fitted with flash eliminators, there's still a danger of the enemy observing your position with every round you fire. Once again, stay well back to stay safe.

Never cross an open space directly. Always take the long way round if that lets you stay in cover. If you must be out in the open at all, make it as short a time as possible.

If the whole of your fire team is on the move, don't cross open spaces one at a time: the first man may get through, but it will give any enemy a good opportunity for an aimed shot at anyone following on. Move as a group, and use smokescreens and covering fire. It does make for a bigger target, but this technique still reduces the risk to a minimum.

When you have to cross alleyways and narrow streets, spread out into a line, with three to five metres between one another. On the squad leader's signal, all cross together – fast!

As soon as you have taken up your new position you nust be ready to give covering fire to the other members of your squad, and that means you have

**Watch your feet**
Basement windows can be a source of danger, too. Keep a careful look-out for them, and always be sure that you don't expose your legs to view. Make sure to jump well clear of the window, or use whatever is available to step above it. Even if you get past unhurt, the next man may not.

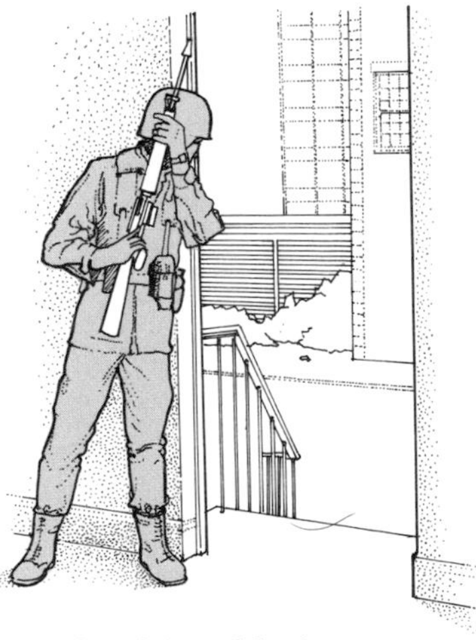

**Stand clear of the doors**
Don't use doorways if you can avoid it – they are just too obvious as targets. If there really is no alternative, be sure to pick out your next position before you set out.

**Keep covered**
Don't ever do anything as obvious as leaving a house by way of the door without covering fire from at least one of your team. And be sure that the position you move to will allow you to cover him, when it comes to his turn to move.

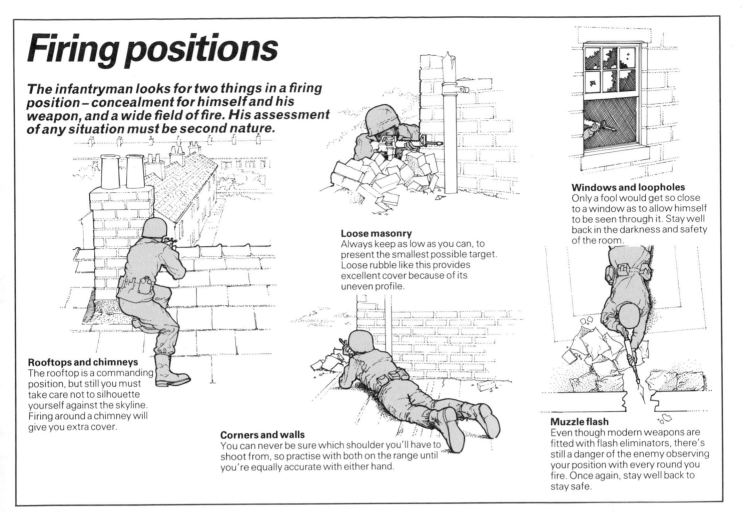

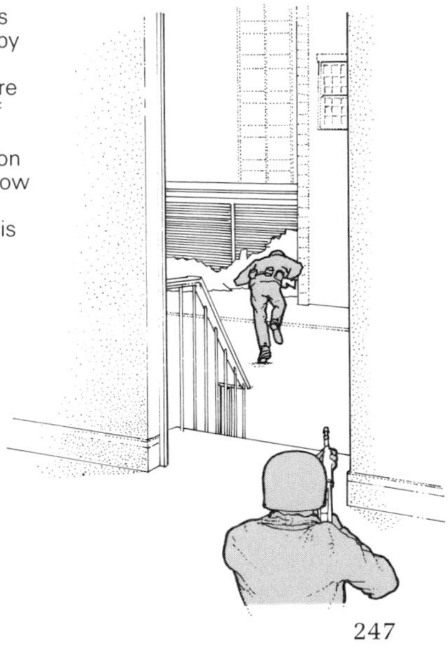

# Moving as a fire team

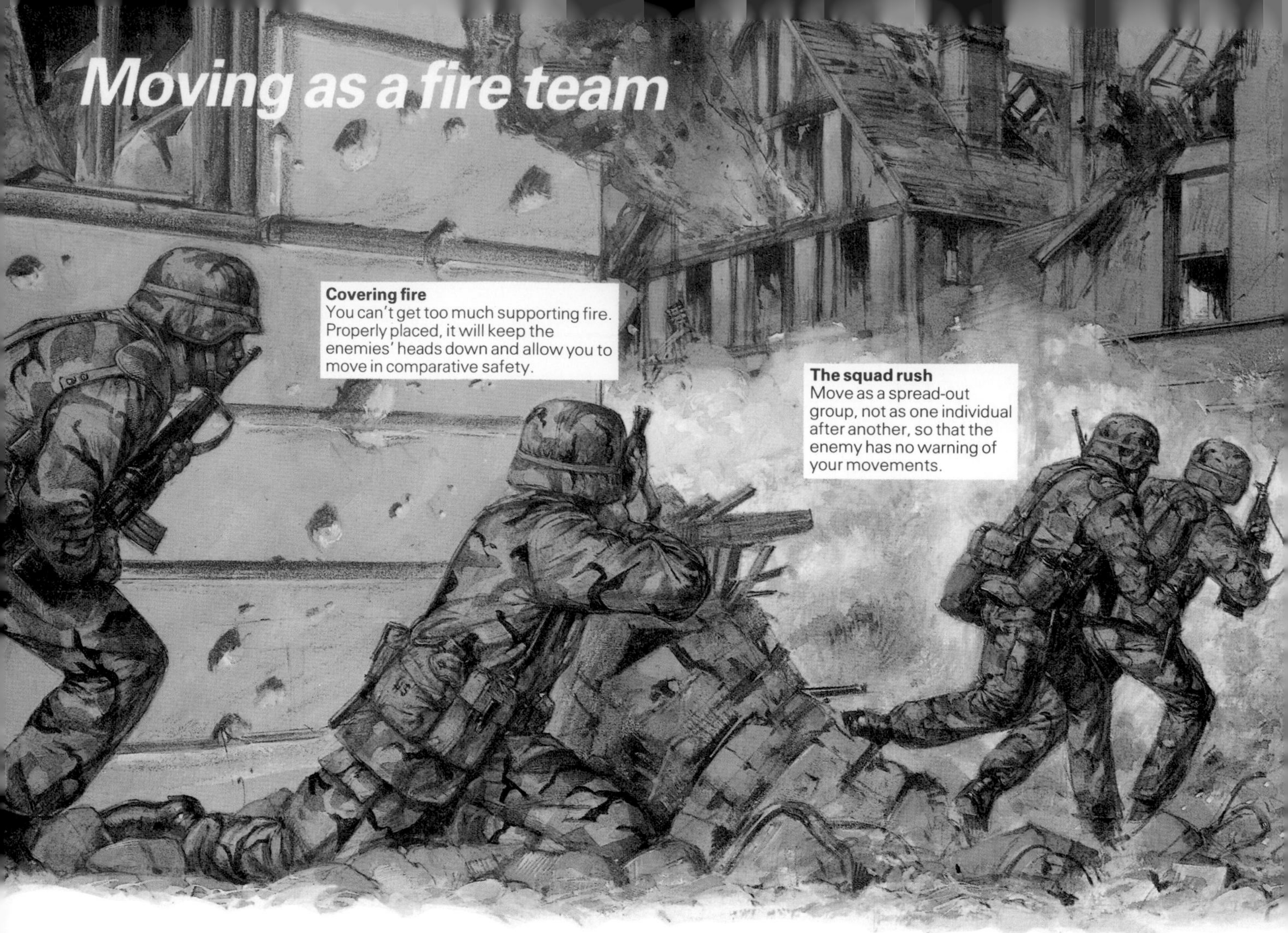

Covering fire
You can't get too much supporting fire. Properly placed, it will keep the enemies' heads down and allow you to move in comparative safety.
The squad rush
Move as a spread-out group, not as one individual after another, so that the enemy has no warning of your movements.

to be ready to use your weapon from either shoulder. Never, ever fire over the top of your cover. You will be silhouetted against the building or sky behind. Always fire around your cover and don't take any chances by exposing yourself to enemy fire. Take every chance you can to practise firing your weapon from the shoulder that you don't normally use – you never know when you'll need to be able to do this.

## Firing positions

The individual rifleman succeeds or fails in his job through how he chooses and uses firing positions. There are two things to keep in mind: how to put fast, accurate fire down on to the enemy position, and how to avoid exposing yourself to return fire.

In attack you will almost certainly have to use improvised methods called 'hasty firing positions'. These may be from round the corners of buildings, from behind low walls, through windows, from behind roof ridges and beside chimneys, and through holes blown in walls by heavier weapons.

## Don't stand up

When firing from round the corner of a building, don't use the standing position. This will place too much of your body in view and your head will be precisely at the height the enemy expects it to be. Kneeling is good, but lying down is better.

Fire around walls, from as low a position as possible, and try to use any rubble or fallen stones and bricks to give extra cover.

The most common mistake made when firing from a window is to get too close to it, in order to widen your field of fire. You won't be able to give your full attention to a field of fire that

***When the time comes to move, do it quickly, with no hesitation. These US Marines of Company H, 2nd Battalion are seen closing in on a group of VC during the battle for Hue.***

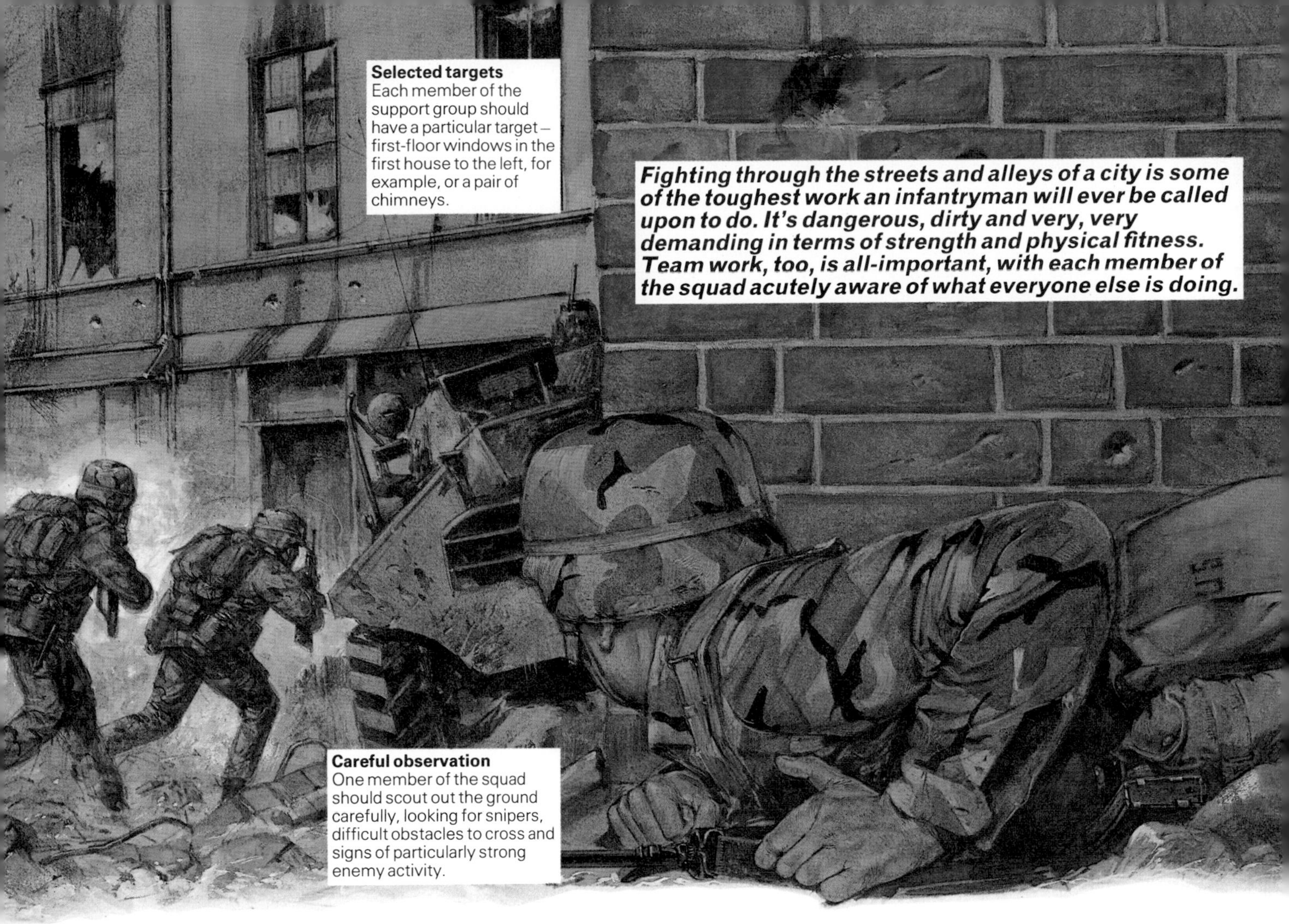

Selected targets
Each member of the support group should have a particular target – first-floor windows in the first house to the left, for example, or a pair of chimneys.
Careful observation
One member of the squad should scout out the ground carefully, looking for snipers, difficult obstacles to cross and signs of particularly strong enemy activity.

***Fighting through the streets and alleys of a city is some of the toughest work an infantryman will ever be called upon to do. It's dangerous, dirty and very, very demanding in terms of strength and physical fitness. Team work, too, is all-important, with each member of the squad acutely aware of what everyone else is doing.***

wide, so don't expose yourself to unexpected fire. Stay well back in the room – the end of your rifle muzzle should be at least one metre inside the room, and preferably two. The muzzle flash will then be hard to see, and so will you. Just because you can see out of a window, even from the other side of the room, doesn't mean that an observer on the outside can see that far in. It is almost impossible to see more than a metre inside, unless a room is lit from another direction as well as through the window you are using.

### *Loopholes*

The same rules apply to firing from 'accidental' loopholes – holes that have been blown in walls by fire from heavy weapons. Stay well back inside the room to hide both yourself and the muzzle flash, even though this will reduce your field of fire. Fire from a lying or kneeling position wherever you can.

Roof-top positions are useful. They give you an excellent field of fire, and put the enemy at the disadvantage of having to fire up into the air. Use the side of a chimney or any other side wall or structure to give yourself extra cover, and try not to expose your silhouette straight over the top of the roof-ridge. Remember, when no cover is available, reduce the size of the target you give to the enemy by all or any of these means:

**1** Fire from the lying position.
**2** Fire from the shadows.
**3** Don't present a silhouette.
**4** Use tall grass, weeds and bushes, rubble and ruins to hide in – they won't stop an enemy bullet but they will stop him from seeing you.

## *Alley-crossing as a team*

Open spaces, streets and even narrow alleyways present a greater obstacle to the infantryman than walls or piles of rubble ever can. The procedure is to cross as a group, spread out with three to five metres between one man and the next. Once every member of the squad is in position, the leader gives the order and everyone goes at the same time. That way, the enemy forces aren't given any warning of your intentions.

# Combat Report
## Vietnam: Riverine Patrol Part 1

**Don Montgomery served with the US Navy in Vietnam and manned the forward .50-cal machine-guns on a patrol board in the Mekong Delta. This is his story of one days's patrol, in February 1966.**

It had been a long night, the night of 26 February. I had the dawn watch. Base control had called for our coded position just after I had taken the wheel, and that was the last transmission I had heard for nearly two hours.

It was 07.00 when I woke the patrol officer, Bill Jump, and the boat captain, Benny Benson. We ate a few hot C-rations that we had heated on the exhaust manifolds of the engines. At 07.15 I got on the radio and called for our cover boat to meet us up-river.

As I operated the radio I was looking over the riverbank to the south side, and I noticed an object that seemed to be anchored to the bottom, for it was holding its position even though the tide was moving at over 12 knots.

I hung the radio mike back in its rack and picked up the binoculars from the console dash. It looked like a large coconut wrapped in wire mesh. If our cover boat had come up-river close to the beach, it would have hit it before the crew had seen it.

### Fighter-bombers!

I called Jump's attention to it. He got out an M-79 grenade launcher and fired a round at it. John Sweatman was on the forward gun mount and I passed the M-79 up to him. John fired four rounds and Jump fired seven before they finally got a hit and, even then, it was not a direct one.

Jump hit slightly to the left of it and it exploded with a loud report. There was a large cloud of black smoke, which indicated that it had contained a black powder charge. It was not really a big enough charge to seriously damage a fast-moving PBR, but certainly enough to scare the hell out of its crew. Another example of VC harassment.

At 07.40 John pulled up the anchor and we started up-river at 1500 rpm. It was already getting hot, and the air was still. I relieved John on the main gun mount, and one hour later we made rendezvous with PBR 125. Together we moved upstream to the fish stakes near the eastern end of the cocunut grove. I looped our bow line around the main support of the stakes and 125 came in and tied up alongside. A light breeze started to blow in from the South China Sea and we relaxed. Not a single boat or barge moved on the river – that should have been a warning.

It was 11.30. We could leave station at noon, so we cast off and started up river at a slow idle. We took the lead, 300 metres ahead. I was the first to hear the noise and knew what it was before I turned to look. Off the port quarter three aircraft, prop driven, were coming down in attack formation: fighter-bombers! I called out that I could see the tiger-skin markings on the fuselage – they were South Vietnamese Skyraiders out of Can Tho.

Intelligence had said that there were no large Viet Cong forces in Go Cong province. I didn't have much faith in this idea and these fly boys really wrapped it up. US Intelligence in the Mekong Delta left a lot to be desired.

They passed over our stern, right between the two boats, at tree-top height. Four hundred metres into the coconut grove the first bomb exploded, hurling the remains of a hut into the air. In a couple of minutes the whole grove was covered with purple smoke.

The aircraft looped around and started a second bombing run. This time they dropped their bombs two hundred metres from the beach. We were just opposite a canal that led into the coconut grove when there was a cracking sound forward, and I saw fragments of fibreglass flying off the port side of the boat.

### I opened fire again

I fired several rounds with my M-16 at where I thought the fire was coming from. The patrol officer shouted, "All guns to starboard." I put down the rifle, released the brake on the forward .50s and swung them towards the beach. Shells and bullets were striking all around the boat, but none of us had been hit yet. At last Jump called out, "Fire!".

I pushed down the trigger mechanism. The guns jarred, vibrated and spat forth their message. I sprayed every spot I thought might hide a gun emplacement. Between bursts of gunfire I could hear the radio transmitting:

"Druid Alfa 1 and Druid Alfa 2: bullets are landing all round you. Speed up! Look out, machine-gun firing at your stern!"

I felt the boat accelerate to 1500 rpm. At this speed the boat responded fairly well and still travelled slowly enough for the gunners to shoot straight. I had to stop firing to clear a twisted ammo belt and again I could hear Jump on the radio to CO:

"Druid Base to Druid Alfa: be advised will sortie afternoon patrol early. It will be over an hour before we can reach your location. Can you hold enemy pinned to the beaches? Over."

"Druid Alfa to Druid Base: I don't know. We're using up ammo pretty quick and we're under intense fire from rifles and machine-gun emplacements. Can you get hold of Andy 88 and send him over? If he can get us more air support we can probably hold them for a while."

I opened fire again. Everywhere I looked the VC were running. By now we had run from the canal at the eastern end of the coconut grove to the rice mill at the western end: a distance of 3000 metres, and we had used up nearly a third of our ammo supply. Before the day was over we'd be using the captured guns we had on board.

We decided to conserve ammo until the other patrol could arrive, and concentrate our fire on the heavy gun emplacements. It wouldn't be easy to allow those riflemen to snipe at us, but we had to keep the VC from moving out until we had enough ammo to shoot anything and everything that moved. That was one problem with the PBR: having to patrol with only a small quantity of ammo, you had the speed but you weren't prepared to fight a prolonged engagement. Unfortunately, that was exactly what we were being called upon to do.

**Aircraft pounded the river bank, forcing the VC to keep their heads down and letting us reorganize.**

**A PBR speeds into the Mekong Delta, a labyrinth of tidal waterways and mangrove swamps that had been out of government control for the last 40 years until the US Navy took up the challenge.**

# TAKING OUT ENEMY POSITIONS

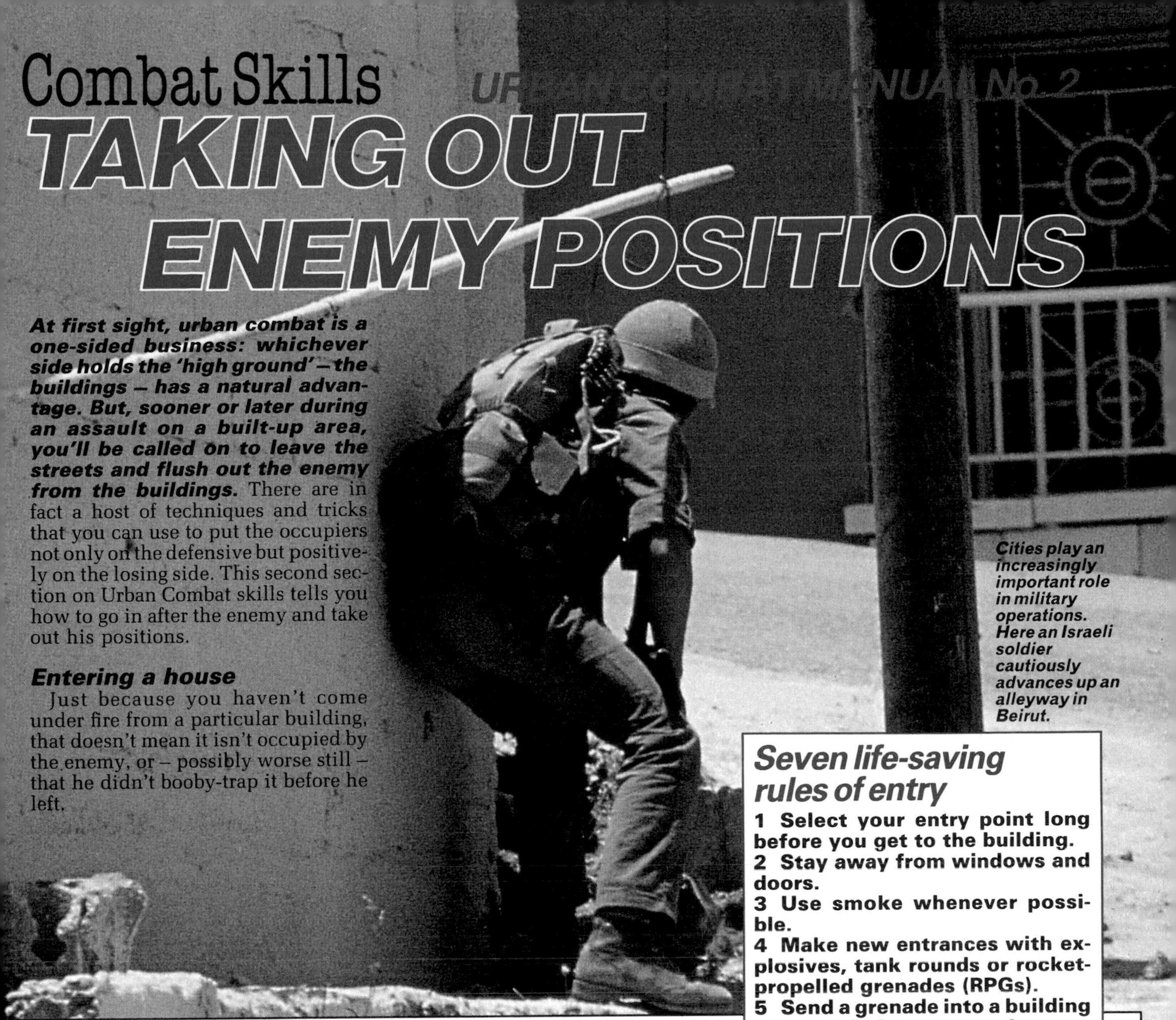

**At first sight, urban combat is a one-sided business: whichever side holds the 'high ground' — the buildings — has a natural advantage. But, sooner or later during an assault on a built-up area, you'll be called on to leave the streets and flush out the enemy from the buildings.** There are in fact a host of techniques and tricks that you can use to put the occupiers not only on the defensive but positively on the losing side. This second section on Urban Combat skills tells you how to go in after the enemy and take out his positions.

## Entering a house

Just because you haven't come under fire from a particular building, that doesn't mean it isn't occupied by the enemy, or — possibly worse still — that he didn't booby-trap it before he left.

*Cities play an increasingly important role in military operations. Here an Israeli soldier cautiously advances up an alleyway in Beirut.*

## Seven life-saving rules of entry

**1** Select your entry point long before you get to the building.
**2** Stay away from windows and doors.
**3** Use smoke whenever possible.
**4** Make new entrances with explosives, tank rounds or rocket-propelled grenades (RPGs).
**5** Send a grenade into a building or room before you go in yourself.
**6** Go in immediately after the grenade has exploded.
**7** Go in under covering fire.

## Movement in buildings

### Entering a room
It takes three men to enter a room safely – one to provide security and two actually to go in. The first man throws in a grenade, and goes in after it has gone off. He flattens himself against the wall while his partner searches the room.

### Mouseholes
A 'mousehole' is a hole about 60 cm wide, blown or cut through a wall as an alternative entrance to a room. Doors are easy to booby-trap so you should try to assault through a mousehole, throwing a grenade in first as usual.

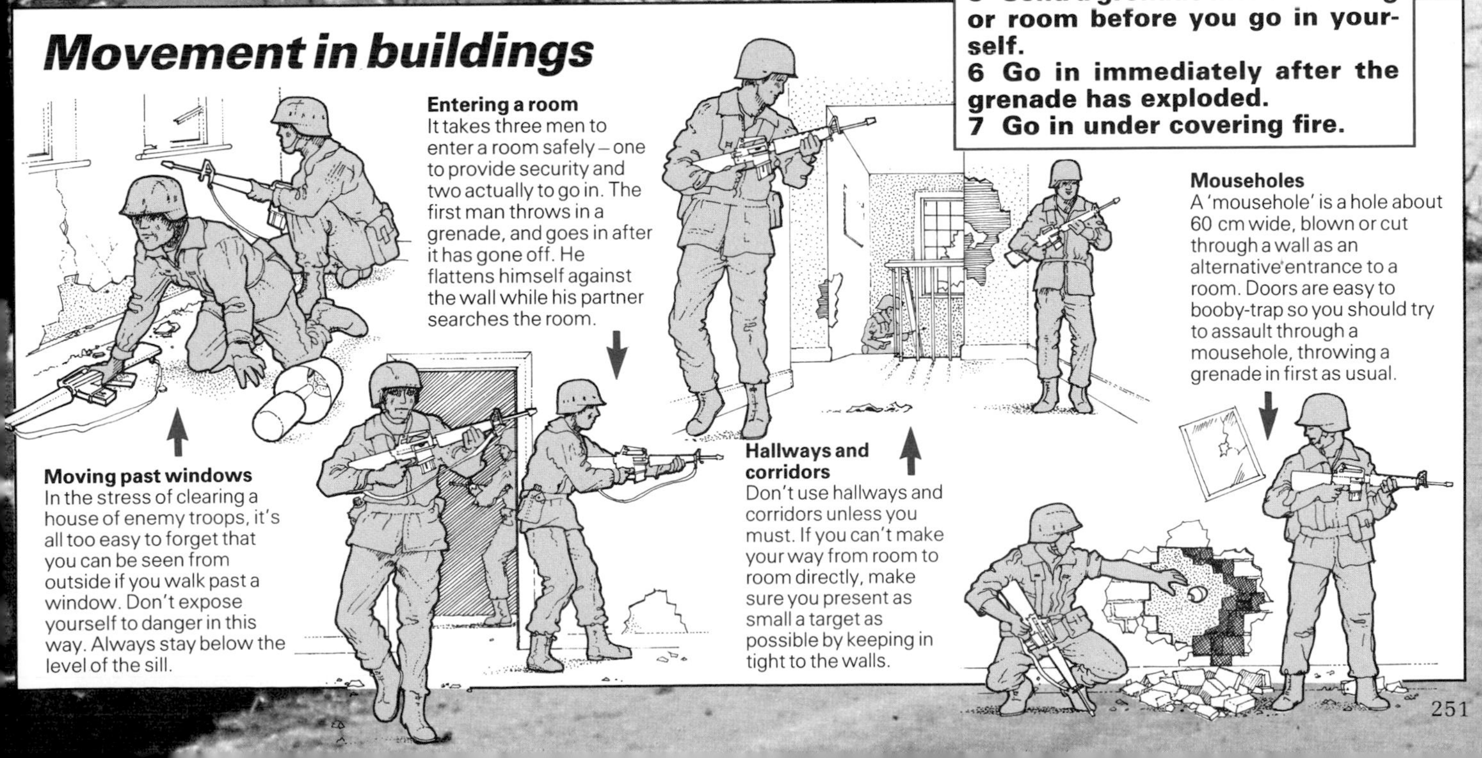

### Moving past windows
In the stress of clearing a house of enemy troops, it's all too easy to forget that you can be seen from outside if you walk past a window. Don't expose yourself to danger in this way. Always stay below the level of the sill.

### Hallways and corridors
Don't use hallways and corridors unless you must. If you can't make your way from room to room directly, make sure you present as small a target as possible by keeping in tight to the walls.

Until you know for sure that a building has been cleared, always assume the worst. Don't go in through the doors or the ground floor windows if you can possibly avoid it. Treat as suspect any hole you haven't blown in a wall yourself.

### Clearing from the top

Although nothing to do with house-clearing can be said to be safe, the best way to do it is from the top. It's a lot easier to fight your way down than up, and it also gives the enemy somewhere to go! If you corner enemy forces on the top floor of a building, they have no alternative but to try and fight their way out. If you drive them down to the ground floor, there's a good chance they'll try to make a run for it – straight into covering fire from the rest of your squad.

Although entering at the top floor of a building does present some problems, they're not as bad as you may think. Once one house is cleared, you have access to the roof of the next. It's only the first house that presents a problem, and that can be solved easily enough if helicopter support is available. Otherwise you can use ladders, drainpipes or, at worse, ropes.

The easiest way to get a rope up to the top floor or roof of a building is with a grappling iron – three or four large metal hooks welded together and attached to the end of a rope. Don't use too thin a rope; although it will weigh less, it is much more difficult to climb than a thick one. You can knot the rope every 30 cm or so to improvise steps but, if you do, it will not pay out so easily when you throw the hook.

### Watch out for snipers

Remember that you will be extremely exposed to sniper fire while you're climbing the wall. Take as few chances as possible, and spend some

## Throwing a grappling hook

Stand as close to the building as possible to reduce your vulnerability to enemy fire. In your throwing hand you have the hook and a few coils of rope; the rest of the rope is in loose coils in your other hand. The throw itself should be a gentle, upward, lob. Check that the hook has a solid hold before you begin to climb. Knotting the rope beforehand at 30 cm intervals will make it easier to grip.

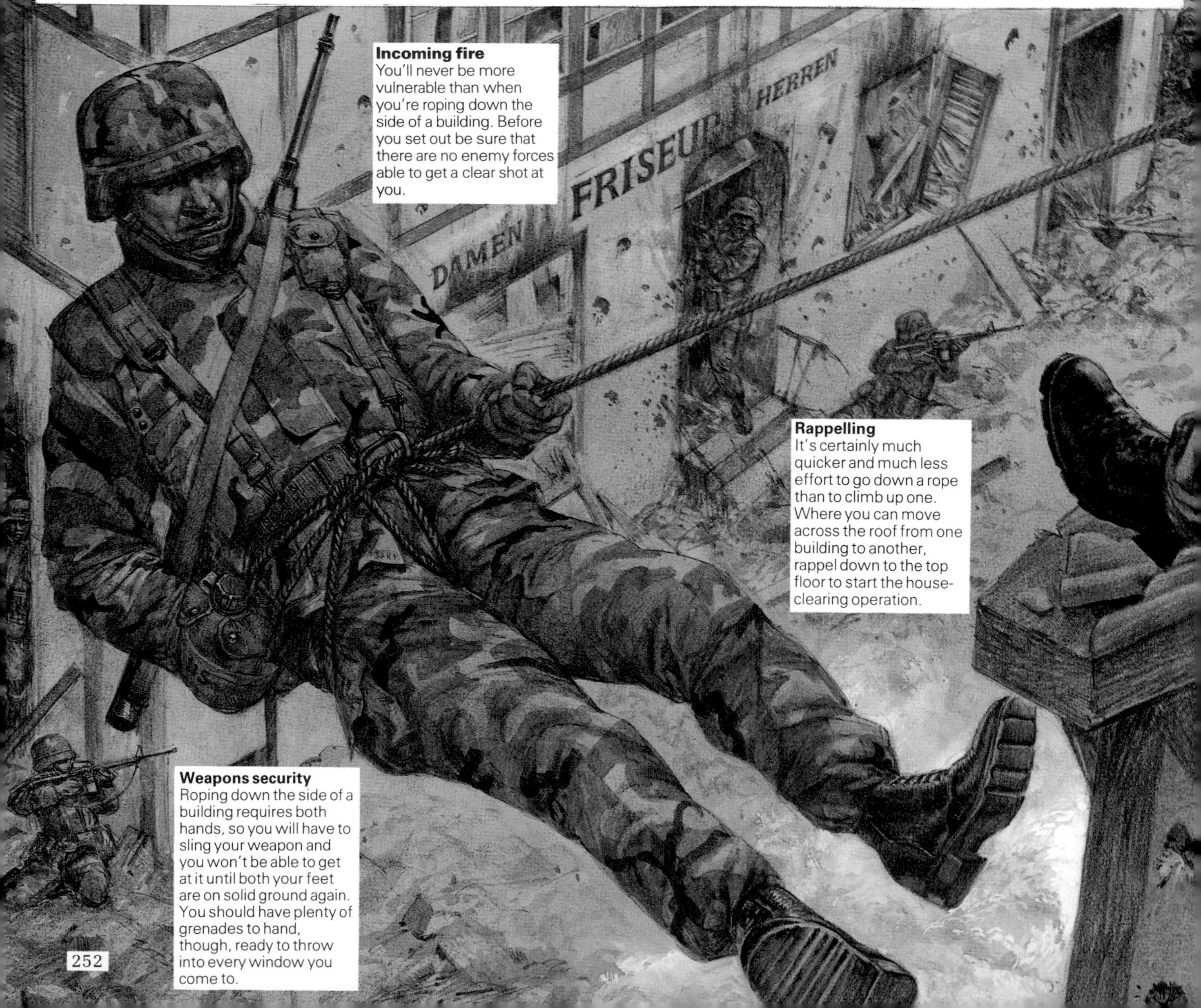


**Incoming fire**
You'll never be more vulnerable than when you're roping down the side of a building. Before you set out be sure that there are no enemy forces able to get a clear shot at you.

**Rappelling**
It's certainly much quicker and much less effort to go down a rope than to climb up one. Where you can move across the roof from one building to another, rappel down to the top floor to start the house-clearing operation.

**Weapons security**
Roping down the side of a building requires both hands, so you will have to sling your weapon and you won't be able to get at it until both your feet are on solid ground again. You should have plenty of grenades to hand, though, ready to throw into every window you come to.

**Anchor points**
The rope should be securely tied off – use the chimney or something similar as your anchorage. In an emergency choose the two biggest, strongest men in the squad to hold on to the rope, and make sure they are in the best possible position before you go over the edge.

time before the attempt in checking any possible sniper positions – and have them cleared.

If you do have to go past windows on the way up, give them a grenade when you're still below the level of the window sill, and always put a grenade through the window you're going to enter.

It is much easier to come down a rope than go up one. When you can, go up to the roof level, staying well down from the ridge so you don't present your silhouette, and rope down to the entry window.

## Rappelling

The US Army uses the French name for roping down: rappelling. It's also known as abseiling. There are a lot of different ways of doing it, but they all rely on the friction of the rope across your body and through your (gloved) hand. A 'free' rappel, where there is no wall to bounce off to slow your descent, is used to come down from a helicopter that has no room to land.

Rappelling needs practice. When you're on the rope you're on your own. If you make a mistake and fall, no-one can save you. Practise in a group with an experienced teacher, and start off low – from a height that won't injure you if you fall. Never try it alone, or without the right equipment.

# Making a sling rope seat

Rappelling, also known as abseiling, is used to descend from the roof of a tall building and in through a window. Urban fighters should be familiar with the sling rope seat.

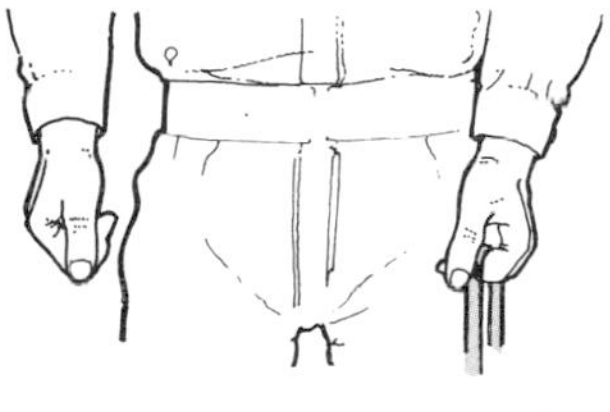

**1** Place the centre of the sling rope on the hip opposite your brake hand. If you are right-handed, use your right hand as the brake hand; if you are left-handed, use the left.

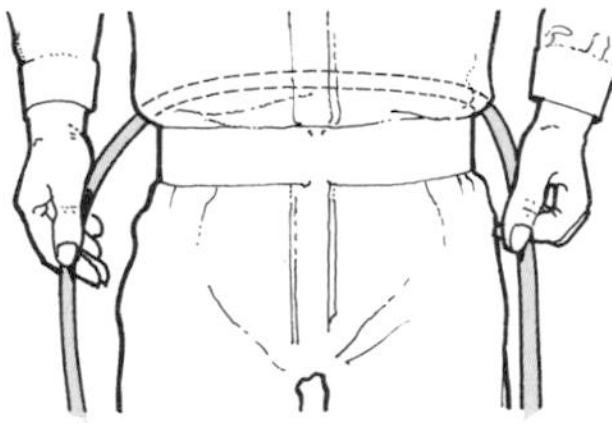

**2** Wrap the rope around your waist, keeping the centre of the rope on your hip.

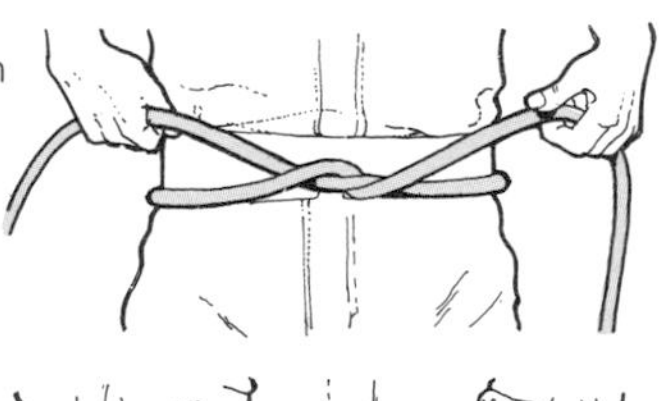

**3** Tie an overhand knot in front of your body.

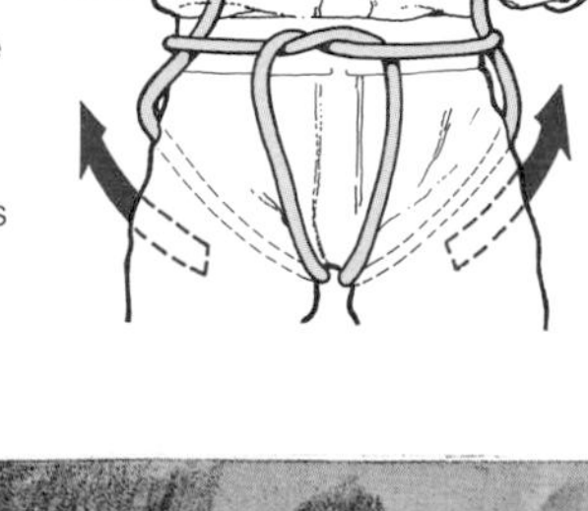

**4** Bring the ends of the rope between your legs, front to rear, then around your legs and under the waist loop.

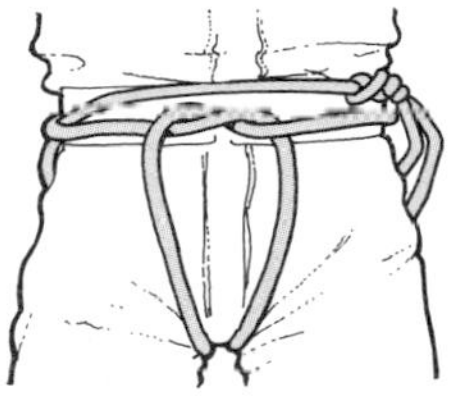

**5** Tie the ends with a square knot and two half-hitches on the side opposite the brake hand. Tuck the loose ends into a pocket.

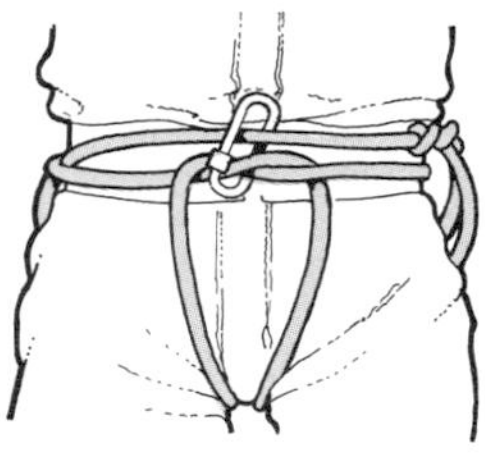

**6** Place the snaplink through the single rope around your waist and through the top ropes that form the overhand knot. Insert the snap link with the gate down and the opening towards the body.

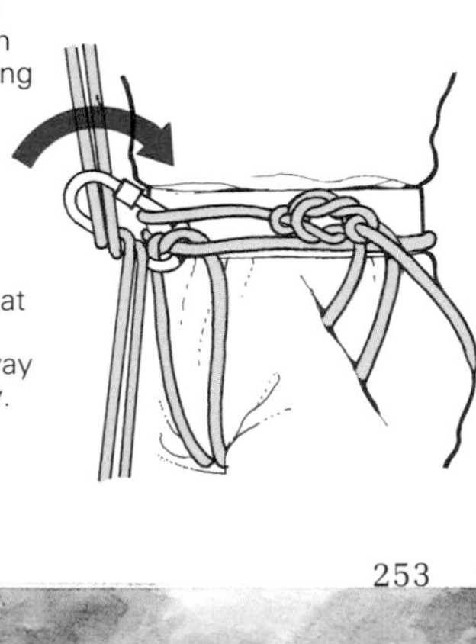

**7** Rotate the snap link one half-turn so that the gate is up and opens away from the body.

Not all your fire team may be able to see you while you're rappelling down, so you must give them a clear signal, both when you start the descent, and when you finish. Where noise doesn't matter, shout 'On Rappel' and 'Off Rappel'. In a situation requiring a silent approach, work out a system of tugs on the rope, and make sure everyone understands it.

### *Through the window*

When you come to the point of entering the window, you can get in very quickly by positioning yourself just above, throwing in the grenade, and then bounding the last couple of feet. If you have to enter while climbing the rope, go up above the sill so that gravity helps you down through the window and into the room. Even after you've thrown in a grenade, you have to get through the window as quickly as possible.

In house clearance, it's always a good idea to 'cook-off' the grenade before throwing it in the window. Grenades have timed fuses to prevent them from exploding in your hand as soon as you pull the pin. If you don't want to throw it too far – just drop it into a room, for example – you need to use up a part of this delay before you throw the grenade. Pull the safety pin and let the firing clip go. Then count 'One thousand and one, one thousand and two,' before throwing the grenade. This will use up two seconds of the delay and reduce the chance of someone throwing it back!

You should never throw a grenade without a secure place for you to shelter. Once a grenade has left your hand

**_In urban combat part of the squad advances; the other men cover possible enemy positions. This picture was taken during house-to-house fighting in Managua, Nicaragua, in 1979._**

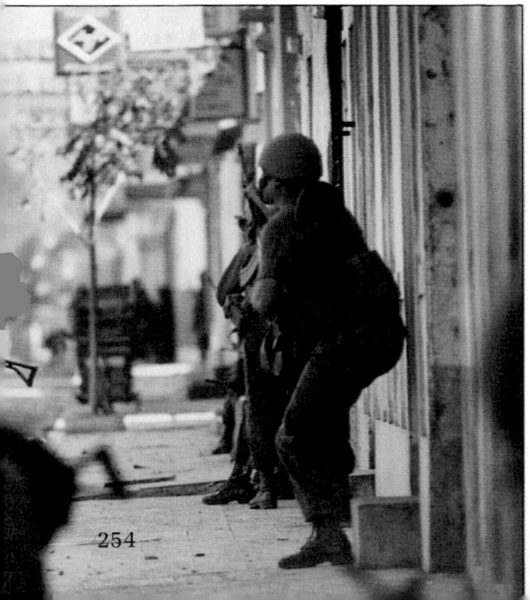

## *Ground-level entry*

Don't use doors and windows if you can avoid it. Here are three methods of entering a building via windows.

**1 Two-man lift**
Two men bend down facing each other with cupped hands or holding a plank. They support the climbing man as he reaches for the window sill and lift him upwards so that he can climb in.

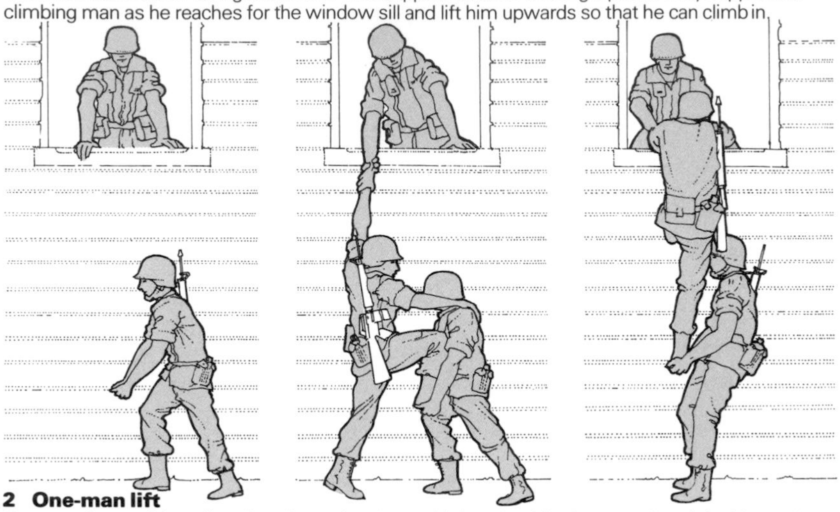

**2 One-man lift**
One man braces himself against the wall and cups his hands while the man already inside reaches down. Together they help the climbing man through the window.

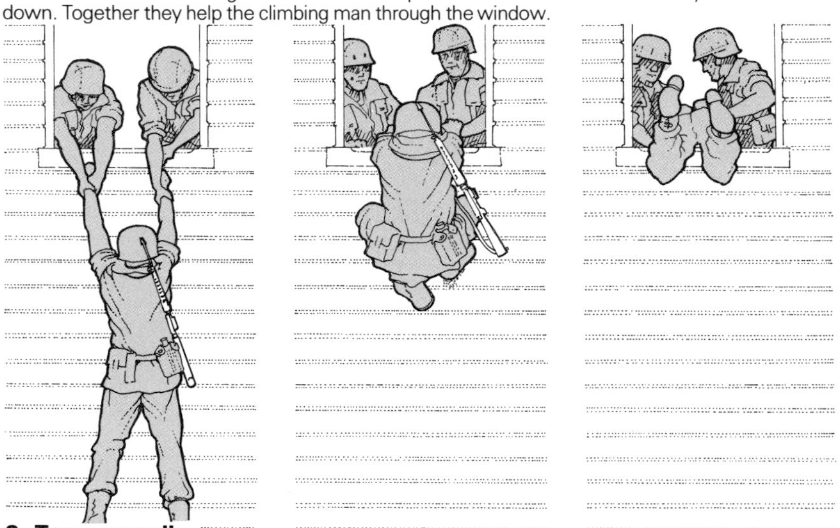

**3 Two-man pull**
Once the first two men are inside, they can pull the third man up by his hands as he scrambles up the wall.

it is a very unpredictable weapon. It could take a bad bounce or explode prematurely. If you can, use a grenade launcher such as the M203 attached to the M16 rifle, or the bulkier M79 grenade launcher. These two weapons propel a grenade much further and more accurately than you can throw one.

Once again, speed means safety. After you have completed the standard tactic of throwing a grenade in first, you must be through the window as quickly as possible. If the window is above your head you will need the help of one or two members of your squad to push you into the room. Remember that it is always safer to call up armoured or RPG support if you can. Such heavy weapons can knock a hole in a wall for you to enter the building at a point the enemy could never have considered when he set up his defences.

# CLEARING AN ENEMY-HELD BUILDING

***When you're inside a house where enemy troops are installed, the grenade takes over from the gun as your first-line weapon. When clearing buildings – perhaps the most dangerous job an infantryman is called on to do – there's no time to wonder how the enemy's going to react.*** You have to do it to them before they do it to you. And do it quickly, safely and surely, risking your life and those of your team as little as possible.

This section of the urban combat manual looks at clearing buildings room by room, and setting up defensive positions once that task has been completed.

## Watch the outside

There are two problems involved in moving about in buildings occupied by enemy troops – and only one of them comes from inside. The essential point for a soldier to remember in house clearance operations is that enemy forces on the outside are just as dangerous to you as those on the inside. Never stand at windows, in doorways or in holes blown through walls. If you do have to cross in front of windows that could be targeted by the enemy, either keep well back in the room or crawl beneath the level of the window sill.

Inside the house, the danger zones are found in hallways and corridors. The rooms opening on to these are useful hideouts for enemy troops who can then ambush the forces clearing the building. If you are forced to use an entrance hallway or upstairs corridor, always present yourself as the smallest target possible by flattening yourself against the wall. If you come to a turning, treat it as you would a

## REORGANISING YOUR FORCES

**When you have completely cleared the building, you should:**

1. **Resupply and redistribute your ammunition.**
2. **Mark the building so that friendly forces will know it is safe.**
3. **Provide covering fire for assaults on other buildings.**
4. **Treat and evacuate any wounded.**
5. **If the building is to remain occupied, organise a defensive position.**

## SECURING UPPER FLOORS

***As the rest of the team storm into the enemy-held building, a security detachment is left on the roof to guard against enemy counter-attack. The assault team blows a hole in the roof or adjoining wall using a demolition charge, and begins to clear the building from the top downwards. Further demolition charges can be used to blow holes in floors so that the stairs, which may be booby-trapped, need not be used.***

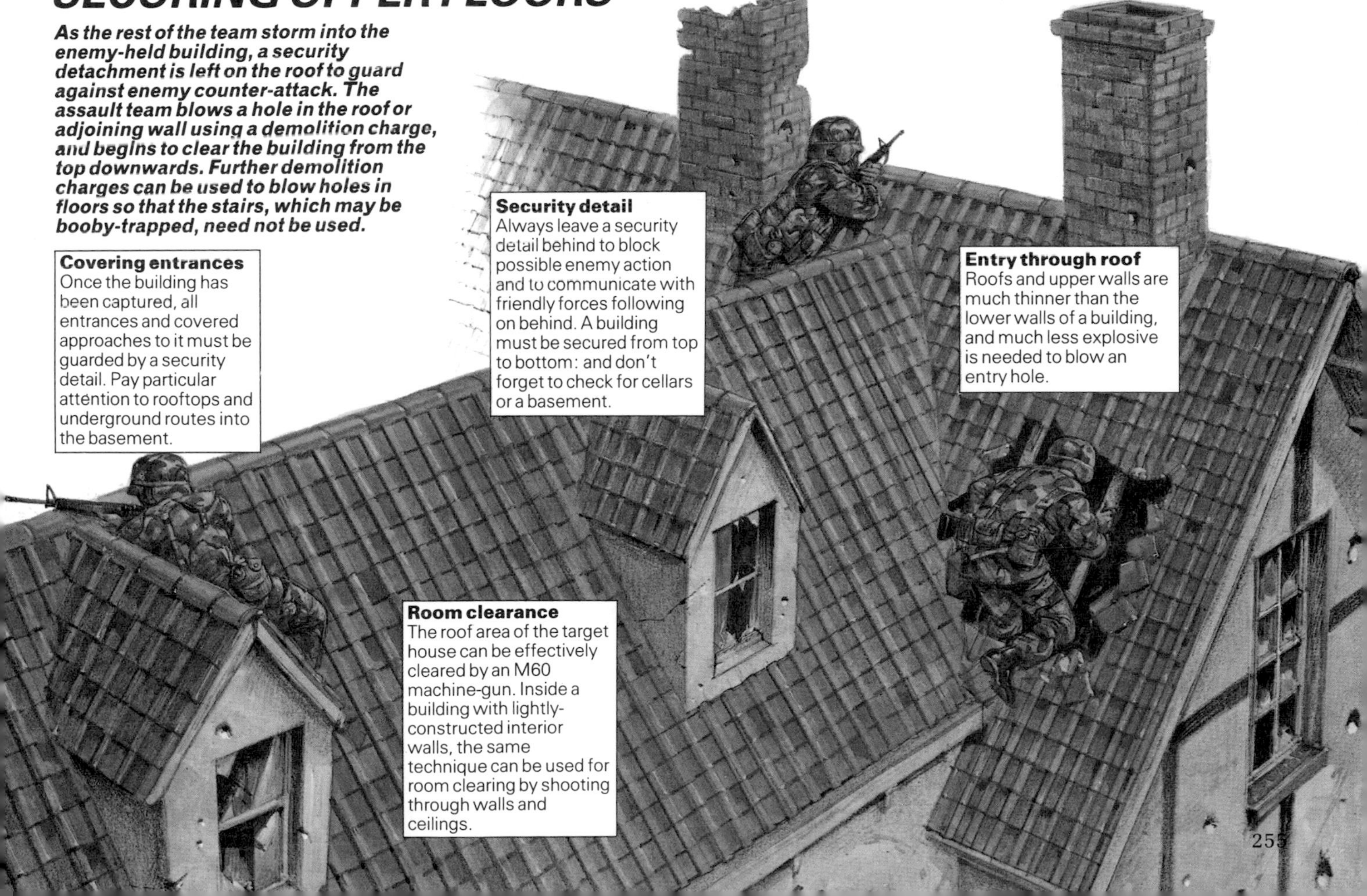

Security detail
Always leave a security detail behind to block possible enemy action and to communicate with friendly forces following on behind. A building must be secured from top to bottom: and don't forget to check for cellars or a basement.
Entry through roof
Roofs and upper walls are much thinner than the lower walls of a building, and much less explosive is needed to blow an entry hole.
Covering entrances
Once the building has been captured, all entrances and covered approaches to it must be guarded by a security detail. Pay particular attention to rooftops and underground routes into the basement.
Room clearance
The roof area of the target house can be effectively cleared by an M60 machine-gun. Inside a building with lightly-constructed interior walls, the same technique can be used for room clearing by shooting through walls and ceilings.

***Fire-escapes are useful avenues of approach from top or bottom and they are usually situated at the back of a building where there is more cover for the assault team.***

room. Never make any assumptions until you have seen for yourself.

When you are approaching a room always keep a sharp eye out for booby-traps. These aptly named devices are hidden bombs with disguised trigger mechanisms. Although they are normally left behind by enemy forces after they have evacuated a position, they have proved useful in the defence of buildings as well.

Constantly bear in mind a few simple rules and you will avoid being a booby. Never touch everyday household objects such as light switches or door handles. Don't be tempted by attractive souvenirs, for their appearance can be deceptive. A handsome gold watch lying on a table could in reality be the trigger to an anti-personnel bomb underneath the furniture. Watch your feet: a favourite location for booby-traps is where you have to walk – the treads of a staircase, for example.

If possible take the most difficult route; it could save your life. Bear in mind that the enemy may have had as long as he wanted to place booby-traps, and don't ever try to render these bombs safe – that is the engineers' job. If you do find a booby-trap, mark its position with tape, chalk or aerosol paint, and give it a wide berth.

### Go for the grenade

Infantrymen are taught in basic training that their rifle is their best friend. However, when the soldier is clearing a house the grenade replaces the rifle in his affections. Its explosive strength is increased by the small enclosed spaces, and it provides a quicker source of firepower in a situation where speed is safety.

When you are ready to enter a room, don't use the doorhandle; it could be booby-trapped and its movement warns the enemy who might be inside that you're about to come in. Instead put a short burst of automatic fire through the door and kick it open. If it is a stout door, get a shot-gun and load it with solid charges. Blast the hinges and then kick the door.

The first thing through the door is not your foot but a grenade. Let it 'cook off' first: pull its pin, wait two seconds, and then throw it in. Be very careful of thin walls, however – grenade fragments can penetrate them and injure you or one of your comrades.

## Fighting from room to room

***Clearing an enemy-occupied building demands split-second timing and practised teamwork. Make full use of grenades and demolition charges, and remember that you can fire straight through thin walls and ceilings – but remember too that the enemy can do the same.***

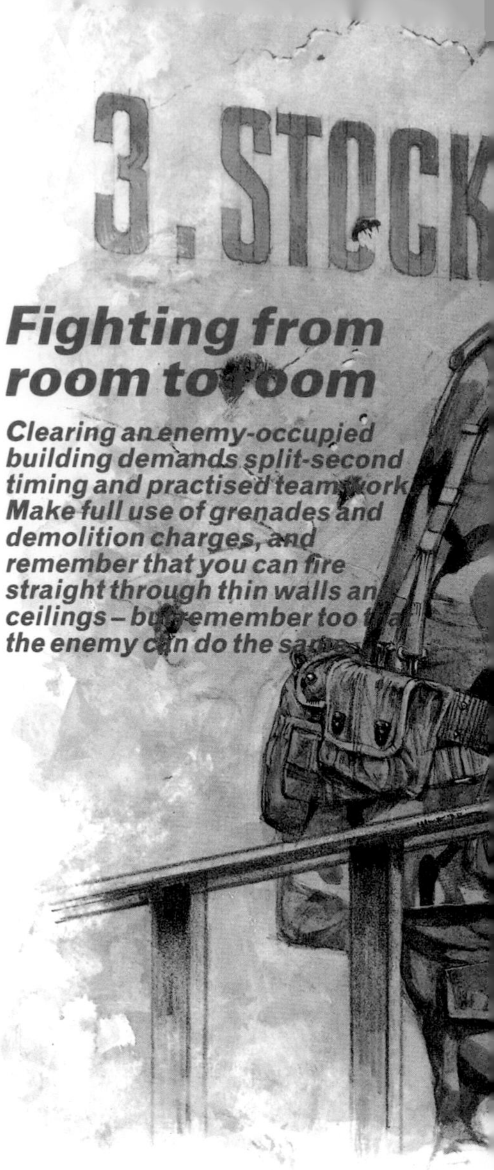

## BEWARE OF BOOBY-TRAPS

It is dangerous to relax after you have cleared a building of enemy troops: they may have left booby-traps behind. These diagrams show favourite positions for anti-personnel devices.

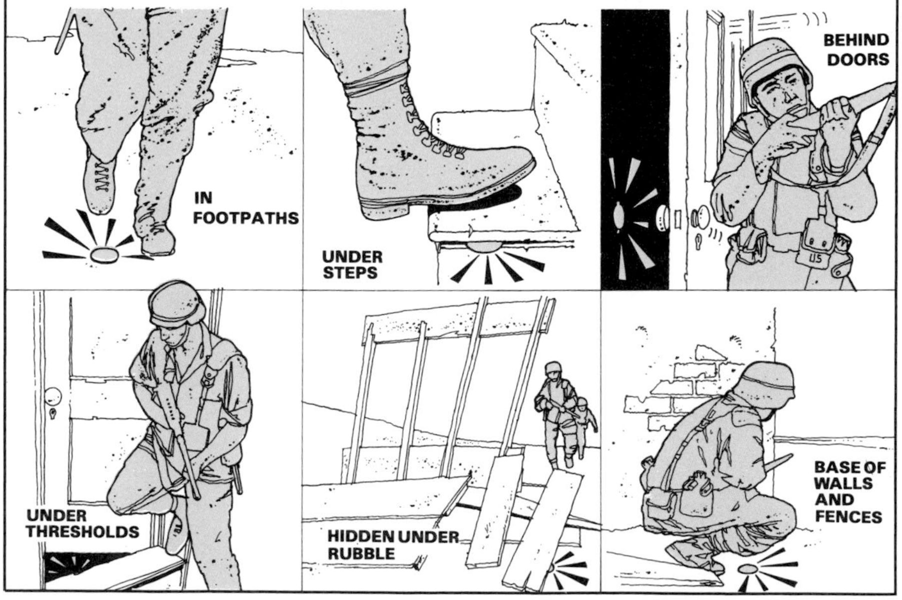


### Bursts of fire

Rush in fast, as soon as the grenade has gone off in the room, firing a short burst from your weapon. The first man in must get his back to the wall, in a position where he can engage any target in the room. Don't try to get off single, aimed shots. Two- or three-shot bursts are more effective. The second man into the room searches it carefully. He is protected not only by his teammate inside the room with him, but also by a support party outside the door.

Always shout messages to your support party. Keep them informed. When you're sure that the room is clear, say so in a loud voice; when you're coming out, once again yell a warning. The same applies to movement up and down staircases.

Don't make the mistake of setting up a pattern as you move from room to room. A clever enemy, lying in wait for you, would be able to work out exactly what you are going to do and when. Instead, vary the way you tackle each room. Use demolition charges or light anti-tank weapons to blow holes in sections of walls so that you can enter from an unexpected direction: but always lead off with a grenade. When a room has been cleared, mark it with tape, spray paint or chalk.

### Keep what you've won

Once a building has been secured, it may be necessary to prepare its defence. Barricaded windows, fortified loopholes, sniper positions, anti-tank positions and machine gun posts are all examples of the sort of hardened firing positions you will need. Each one has different needs and they will be examined in turn.

When barricading a window, leave just a small port through which to put fire on to the enemy. You can use

*A sniper takes aim from a position concealed by shadow. If you are going to prepare a building for defence, knock out the glass from the windows and put a wire mesh anti-grenade screen over the gap.*

material taken from the internal walls of the building you've occupied, or – better by far – already prepared bags of sand or earth. Don't just barricade the windows that you want to use as firing positions. You will tell the enemy exactly where you are to be found. Don't make the firing ports that you leave in the barricade square or of an even shape. That, too, makes the enemy's job easier. Reinforce the walls below and to each side of the window. A modern high-velocity round will go straight through a brick wall and still have enough energy left to cause casualties.

## Watching at the window

Remove any glass left in the windows to avoid injury from splinters, but if there are curtains leave them, so long as they don't restrict your view. If possible, put wire mesh up at the windows to keep out grenades. Arrange it so that you can vary and change your position as much as possible. When firing from an upstairs window, for instance, try to have a table or similar piece of furniture close at hand, so that you can increase the angle of fire downwards by standing on it.

Loopholes should be protected in much the same way as windows. Because you have the choice of where to make loopholes. They can often give a better field of fire than windows, and are more difficult for the enemy to spot.

## Floors and ceilings

As well as protecting the walls to the front and sides of your firing position, you can put a double layer of sandbags or similar bullet-absorbent material on the floor under your feet. This is most useful if you're above the ground floor. You can also build a protective roof with a table and more sandbags. Think about camouflage as well as out-and-out protection. Make dummy firings positions to fool the enemy into wasting time and ammunition.

## Sniping points

These points apply to sniper positions as well as to ordinary fire points, but with extra attention paid to camouflage and concealment. Because the sniper operates at ranges of 500 yards and more, his field of fire is very wide, even if he has a very narrow view. Because of this, he can afford to fire through the smallest hole as long as it still gives him a good view. He must take good care that the muzzle flash from his rifle is not visible to the enemy. In this way he can stay undetected for a long time, and make the very most of his value as a weapon.

*Knocking holes in a roof or wall can give you a firing position with a wider field of fire than that provided by existing windows and doors. It is also harder for the enemy to spot where you are shooting from.*

# FIRING ANTI-TANK WEAPONS FROM INSIDE A BUILDING

Although intended primarily for anti-tank action, the following weapons can be very useful in house-to-house fighting. But backblast is a serious problem, and the following steps must be taken; otherwise you are likely to score an own goal. Remember that the minimum range of the TOW anti-tank missile is 65 metres, which restricts its value in urban combat.

1. Remove all glass from the windows in the room.
2. Wet the floor to reduce the amount of debris thrown up by the backblast.
3. All men in the room must wear earplugs.
4. Everyone must be forward of the rear of the weapon when it is fired.
5. Ensure there is no inflammable debris behind the weapon.
6. There must be an open door or at least two square metres of ventilation behind the weapon to allow the backblast to escape.
7. The ceiling must be at least 2 metres high.

Must have 1.2 metres clear behind weapon.

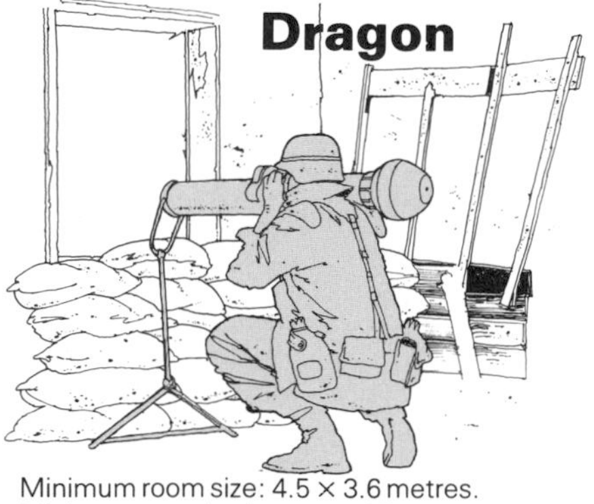


Minimum room size: 4.5 × 3.6 metres.
Minimum muzzle clearance: 16 cm

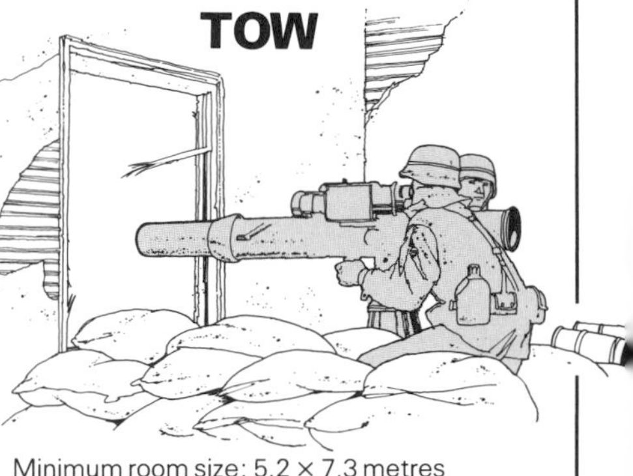


Minimum room size: 5.2 × 7.3 metres
Minimum muzzle clearance: 23 cm

## DUMMY SNIPER POSITION

A dummy position, operated from the ground floor, can be used to draw enemy fire away from the positions that are occupied.

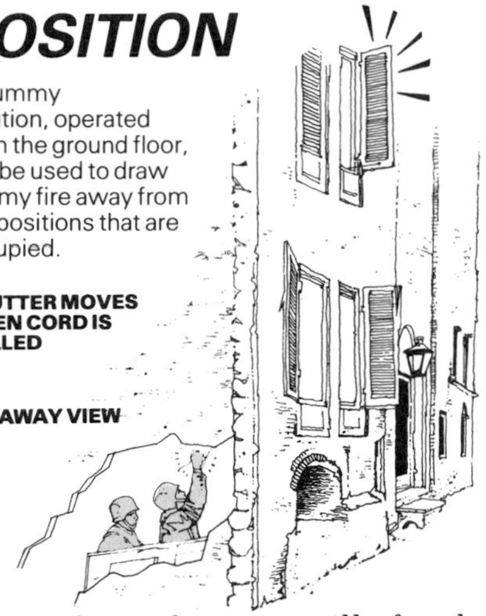

**SHUTTER MOVES WHEN CORD IS PULLED**

**CUTAWAY VIEW**

**Right:** How not to do it – US Marines in house-to-house fighting in Vietnam lean out of the window to shoot at a building occupied by North Vietnamese troops. By pushing his rifle out of the window this Marine is letting everyone know where he is firing from: if at all possible, you should fire from the interior of the room.

An infantry fire team will often be reinforced by an anti-tank squad in urban fighting. The team leader must be aware of the extra needs of the anti-tank gunners, and the partiular difficulties they face when they fire from hiding.

Modern anti-tank weapons are rocket propelled. This means that the round goes in one direction, and a huge blast of flame goes in the other. So it's extremely important to site them in such a way that the back-blast will not injure the crew or other friendly forces. This may often mean the demolition of walls facing away from the direction of the enemy. It will certainly mean that the supporting infantrymen must pay very close attention to where they put themselves when a rocket-propelled weapon is in operation.

### Machine-gun team

Machine guns are the other type of crew-served weapon likely to be attached to fireteams in urban combat. They too deliver heavy firepower and must be protected by the supporting infantrymen, but they are easier to site because there are no problems with back-blast. A machine-gun can utilise a wider field of fire so may need a larger aperture to shoot from. Otherwise, the things to be remembered when choosing a site for it are identical: good concealment, good protection and a good resupply route.

Both anti-tank weapons and machine guns are crew-served: it takes more than one man to operate them. Because of their valuable high firepower, and because their crew members cannot move as quickly under the weight of their weapons should they come under attack, the supporting infantry has to give a high priority to ensuring their safety. They must always be able to give covering fire to their heavier weapons, as well as receiving it.

## IDEAL ANTI-TANK FIRING POSITIONS

***In urban combat, anti-tank weapons are used against enemy-held buildings as well as against tanks.***

Rooftop positions allow anti-tank weapons the greatest field of fire and allow them to be fired at the thinner top armour of enemy tanks. Also, it is difficult for an enemy tank to engage a rooftop target; especially for Soviet armour with its limited main armament elevation.

A Dragon is positioned in a room at the corner of a building so that its backblast is vented out through a window. Corner positions also provide a good field of fire, and are easier to fortify than a rooftop.

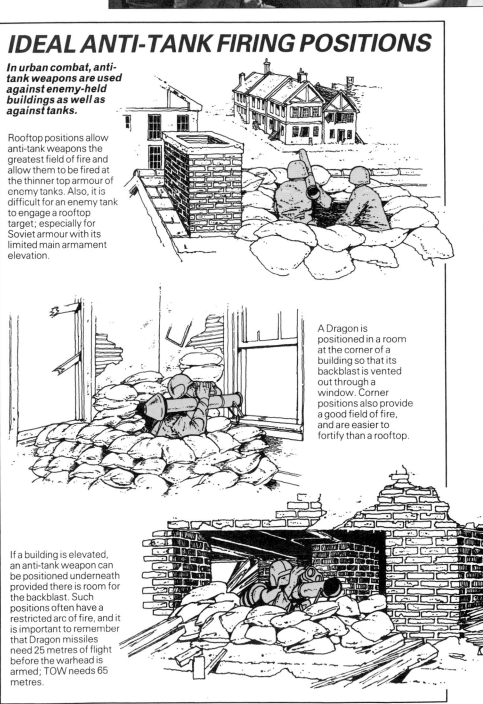

If a building is elevated, an anti-tank weapon can be positioned underneath provided there is room for the backblast. Such positions often have a restricted arc of fire, and it is important to remember that Dragon missiles need 25 metres of flight before the warhead is armed; TOW needs 65 metres.

# Unarmed Combat Course No. 14

# ARMLOCKS AND WRISTLOCKS

***Armlocks and wristlocks are very important techniques. They enable you to defend yourself and to control your attacker; when you've got him in an armlock, you can force him to move wherever you want him to.*** But you should practise only under the supervision of a trained instructor – wristlocks in particular are very painful, and both can lead to a break unless applied with caution.

## Inside wristlock

**1** This wristlock is a good defence against a chest grab. Here, the attacker has grabbed you by the lapel of your jacket.

**2** Reach over with your right hand and grasp the attacker's hand, with your fingers on the inside of his palm and your thumb on the back of his hand.

**3** You then pull his hand away from you and, at the same time, bend it so that the edge of your own hand falls into the crease.

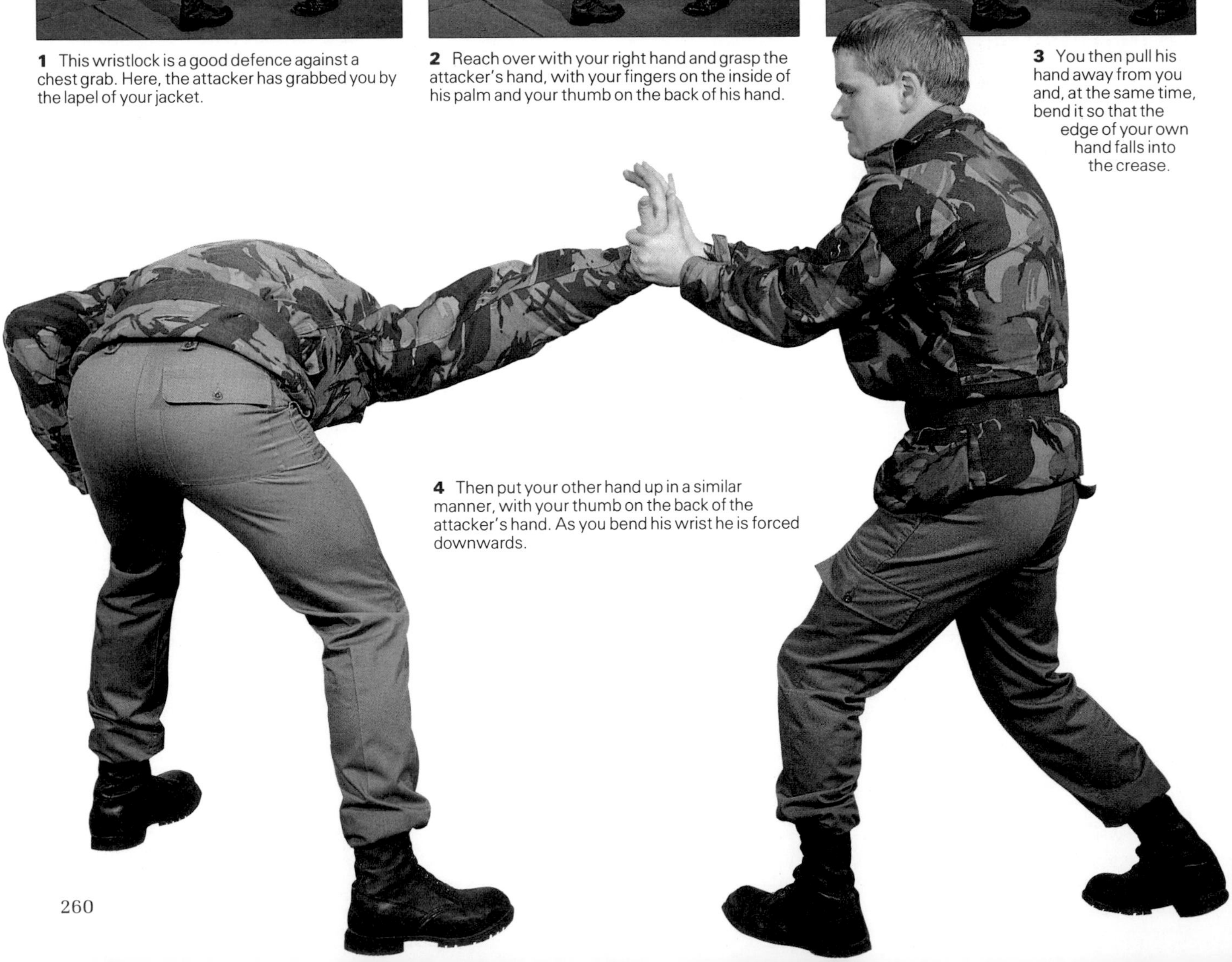

**4** Then put your other hand up in a similar manner, with your thumb on the back of the attacker's hand. As you bend his wrist he is forced downwards.

## Bent armlock

1 Often used as a defence against a blow from above, the bent armlock also works against the elbow joint.

2 Block the attacker's blow, then move your free hand behind the attacker's arm to grasp the wrist of your blocking arm.

3 The attacker is forced on to his back by pressure being applied to his elbow joint. Again, remember that this technique must be practised under trained supervision.

## Straight armlock

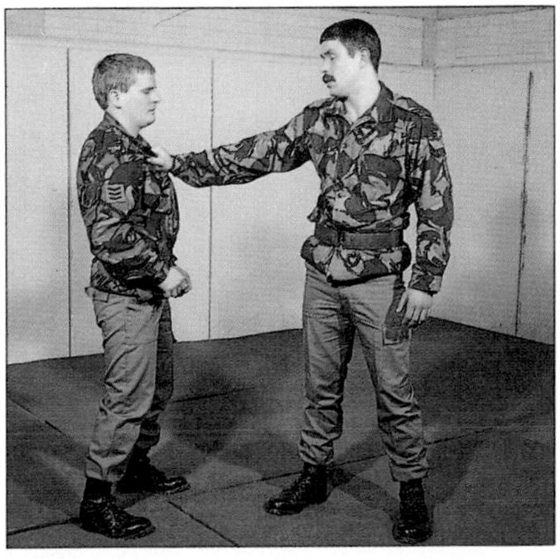

1 The straight armlock, like the others, can be used in a variety of situations, but we will start again with the attacker grabbing your chest.

2 Control the attacker's wrist with your left hand whilst your right hand grabs his fingers and turns his palm upwards, locking his elbow.

3 Keeping the pressure on the attacker's wrist, your own arm is pressed down on the attacker's elbow joint and grasps your own blocking wrist. The attacker is now in a straight armlock.

# Unarmed Combat Course No. 15
# DEFENCE AGAINST A PISTOL ATTACKER Part 1

***If you are faced by a pistol-armed attacker, the odds are all in his favour.*** But fast reactions on your part can defeat him: action is faster than reaction, and if you can manage to get within striking distance, make your move. *Remember: do not use a real firearm in practice.*

## *Inside wrist-strike and blow to chin and groin*

**1** The attacker is pointing a pistol at your chest and forces you to keep your hands up. You slowly close the distance but do not appear threatening.

**2** Suddenly swing your left arm downwards to strike his right wrist and push the gun away.

**3** Knee him in the testicles and smash his chin with the heel of your right hand while your left hand controls his gun arm. Seize the gun before he has time to recover and then step back so that he cannot try the same trick.

## *Handclap strike to wrist*

**1** The attacker is standing in front of you, levelling a pistol at your chest. He has ordered you to put your hands up.

**2** Lower your arms very slowly and move close enough to strike. Again, you must do this carefully and appear frightened, not threatening.

**3** Make a sudden handclap action against his gun hand, making him drop the gun.

# Left body sway and outside wristlock

**1** The attacker is standing in front of you, levelling a pistol at your chest. He has ordered you to put your hands up.

**3** Grasp the attacker's wrist with both hands and apply an outside wristlock.

**2** Move slowly to one side; he will move the pistol to follow you. Then twist at the waist and knock the gun aside with your left arm

**4** Yank the attacker backwards to force him over and make him drop the gun. Seize the weapon and back away.

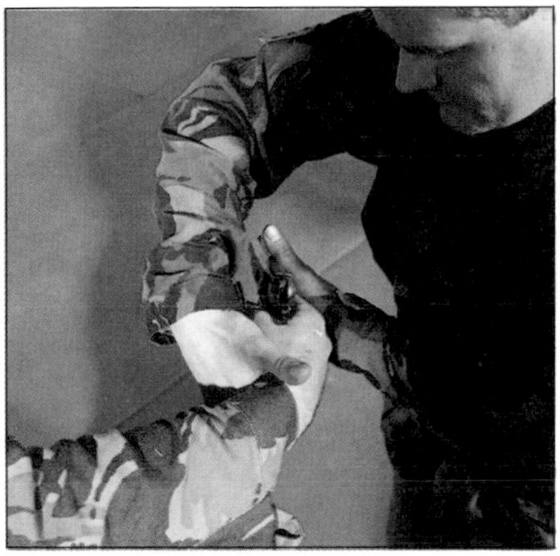

**4** Closeup of the handclap action: one hand strikes his hand holding the gun and the other hits his wrist.

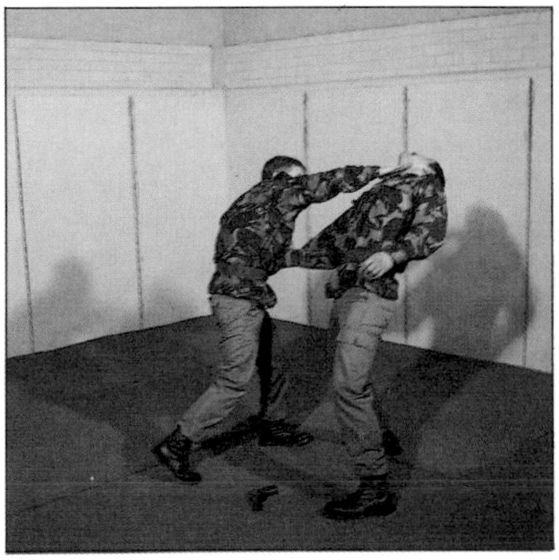

**5** The handclap action is followed up straight away with a blow to the attacker's throat.

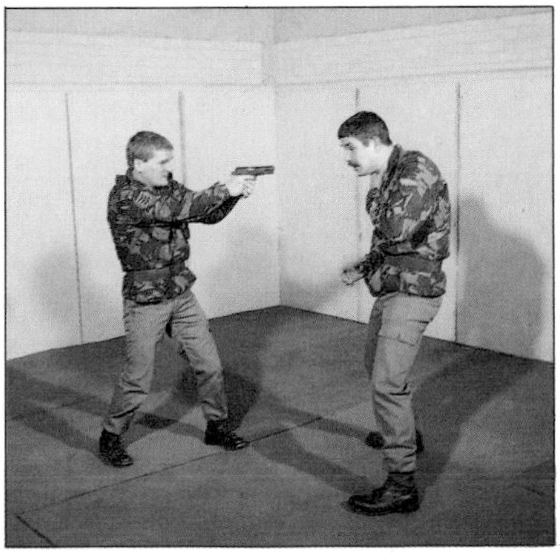

**6** Pick up the gun and back away before the attacker has time to recover.

# Unarmed Combat Course No. 16

# DEFENCE AGAINST A PISTOL ATTACKER Part 2

***These techniques for dealing with a pistol-armed attacker depend on you being close enough to tackle him.*** A humble, frightened attitude will help to convince the attacker that you are not a threat. *Do not use a real firearm in practice.*

## *Inside arm sweep, blow to chin and groin*

**1** If the attacker is behind you, you need to check which hand the gun is in. Glance over your shoulder saying something like, "Where are you taking me?"

**2** Turn smartly to the left and knock his gun arm aside with your left forearm.

**3** Deliver a chin strike with the heel of your hand and simultaneously knee him in the groin. This should enable you to seize the gun, back away and take control of the situation.

# Outside arm sweep and outside wristlock

**1** Again, the attacker is behind you and you need to check which hand the gun is in. If you are both moving, slow down to reduce the gap between you.

**4** With the wristlock properly applied you should be able to throw the attacker over and force him to drop the gun.

**2** Swing sharply to the right and use your right arm to knock his gun arm away from you.

**3** Apply an outside wristlock on his gun hand; remember to get your thumbs side by side as shown here.

# Gun at your head

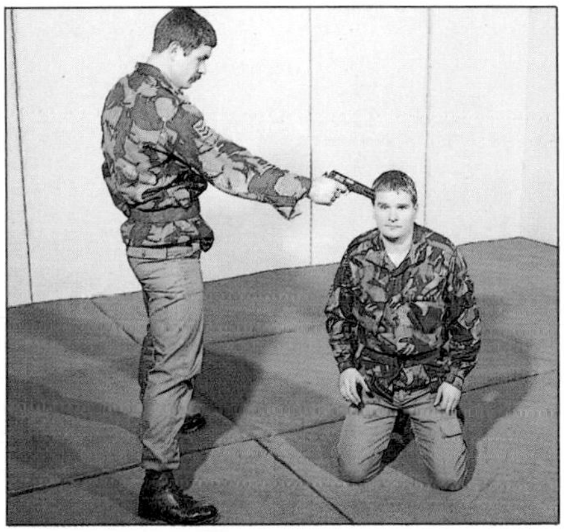

**1** The gunman has ordered you to kneel and places his pistol against your temple. You must react very quickly or it could be too late.

**2** Reach up with your right arm and grab the gun with a 'V' shape of your thumb and fingers as shown here.

**3** Pivot yourself round and bring your other hand up, then bend the gun back towards the attacker.

**4** Pushing your weight against the attacker, you can rise to your feet, pushing the gun further towards the attacker.

# Unarmed Combat Course No. 17

# DEFENCE AGAINST ATTACKER WITH A COSH

***You must tackle an attacker armed with a cosh in the same way as any armed opponent: go for the weapon before the man.*** The defences shown here include basic armlocks as well as more advanced throws.

The defence against a double arm grab is included as another example of a throw being a very effective defence. Remember that a cosh or stick is most dangerous at the tip of its striking arc, so your best defence lies in getting in close.

## *Defence against a swinging cosh*

**1** The attacker comes at you with a cosh and lifts it up, ready to take a swing at you.

**2** From the defensive stance, block his weapon arm using your right forearm.

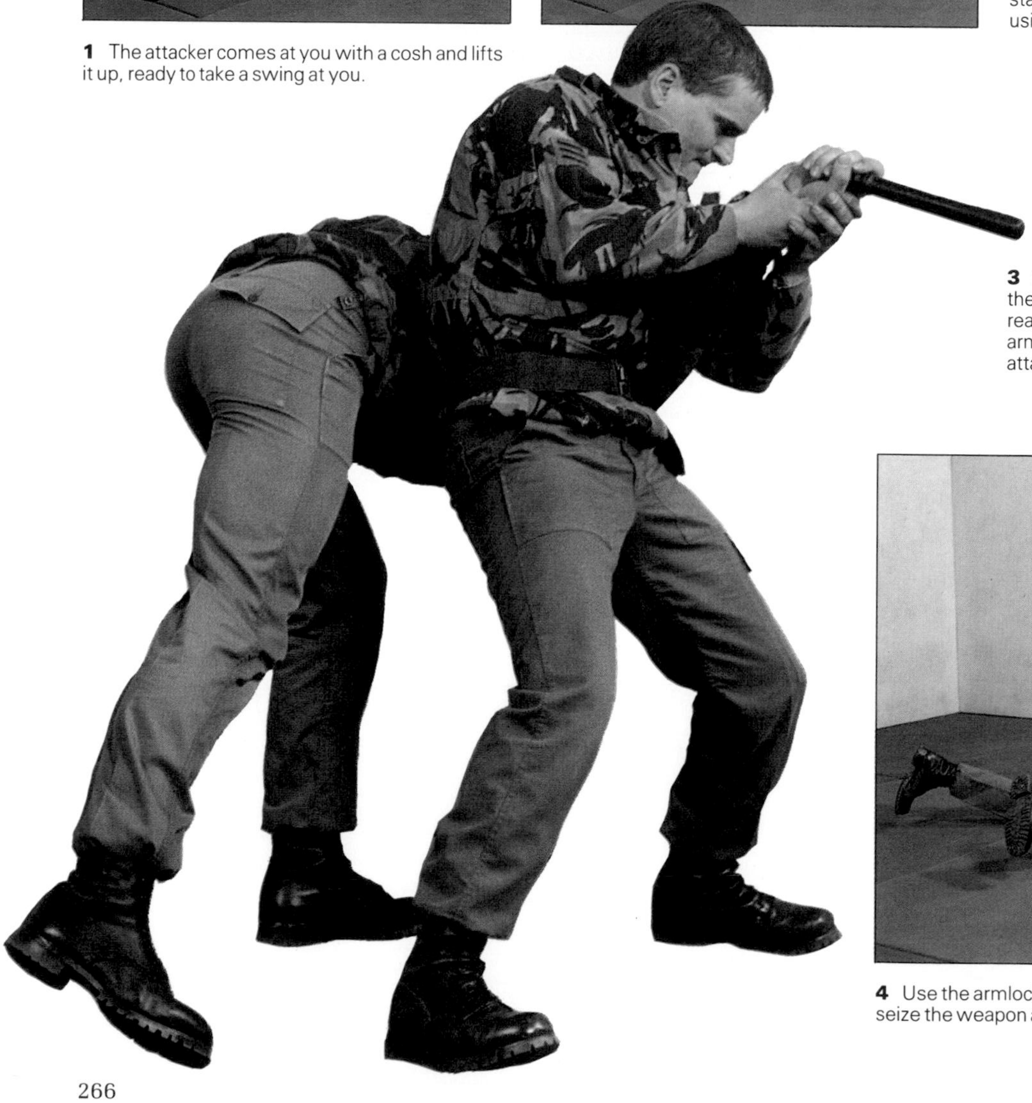

**3** Swing your left arm over the attacker's weapon arm ready to apply a straight armlock and force the attacker to the ground.

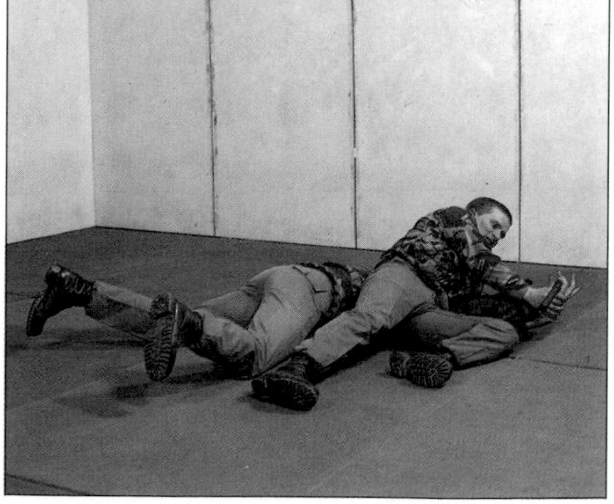

**4** Use the armlock to bring him down; then you can seize the weapon and take control.

# Defence against a double arm grab

**1** The attacker grabs you with both arms from the front. You bring up your arms and grab him just below the shoulders.

**2** Pull back, pushing your right foot deep into his stomach and pivoting back on your left leg.

**3** A smart tug backwards and a good push with your right leg will send the attacker flying upside down. This is a good technique to practise, but do not attempt these moves without trained supervision.

# The body throw defence

**1** The attacker runs at you, preparing to put his full weight behind the blow.

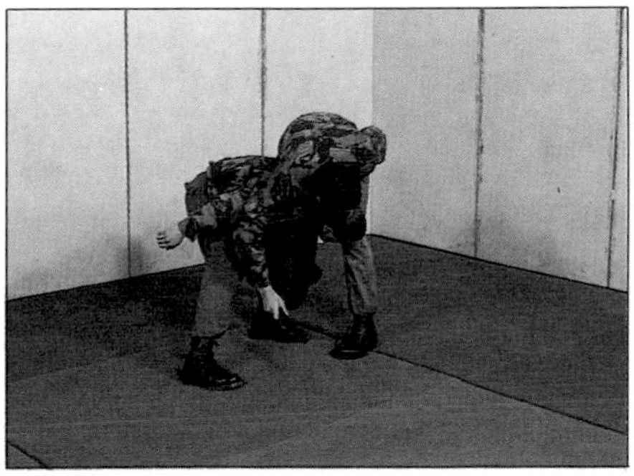

**2** At the last moment you duck right down and he can't help overbalancing.

**3** Suddenly swinging up, you hurl the attacker off his feet using a body throw. Use your arms as well as your back to propel the attacker up and over.

# Weapons and Equipment Guide No. 12

# M60 Destroyer from Detroit

***American armour has had a chequered history since World War II. Although two US armoured divisions, two mechanized divisions and two armoured cavalry regiments provide the nucleus of NATO's military strength in western Europe, it should not be assumed that the 5,000 main battle tanks with which these are equipped are of a universally high standard.***

The first post war tank, the M47, was not a success and, although it was exported or donated to friendly governments around the world, it was never fully adopted by the United States itself. The M48, first produced in 1952, was an improvement, but its 90-mm gun was soon recognised as inadequate.

### *M48 update*

In 1960 the British L7 105-mm gun, built domestically under licence, was fitted to the M48, and by this simple expedient the M60 was born. Manufacture of the M60 proceeded smoothly, with over 3,000 models leaving the Detroit Tank Arsenal production line in the first 15 years alone.

Unfortunately development, if not production, was hindered by Government insistence that priority be given to the fitting of a turret capable of mounting the huge 152-mm Shillelagh rocket system then being trialled, with ominous lack of success, in the Sheridan light tank.

Three hundred new tanks, designated M60A2, were built with the new enlarged turret, whilst a further 243 conventional M60s were converted to the new specification. The 152-mm gun proved to be far too powerful for the chassis, causing acute stabilisation and fire control problems, but, rather than concede defeat, the Pentagon squandered millions of dollars (which would have been far better spent on the development of the M60 itself) in vain attempts to make the M60A2 gun system battle-worthy. When the Shillelagh eventually entered limited service in 1975 it was found to be hopelessly impractical, and was withdrawn almost immediately.

### *International agreement*

In 1963 a tentative agreement was reached between the United States and West Germany to build an advanced tank along radical new guidelines. When national self-interest led to the disintegration of these joint plans, both countries decided independently to continue development. West German plans met with early success with the introduction of the Leopard in 1965 but the United States was less fortunate; it was a full 10 years before the first M1 Abrams was ready for trialling. Although the M60 production continued for an uninterrupted span of 25 years, for much of this period tank development funds were either squandered on the M60A2 Shillelagh or poured into the astronomically expensive M1 Abrams project.

As a direct result the M60 was constantly underfunded and cannot be regarded as a latest generation tank, and although it still forms the backbone of United States' armour (according to the International Institute For Strategic Studies *Military Balance 1986-1987* there are 668 M60s and 7,352 M60A3s in service), it can in no respect be regarded as a match for the Soviet T-64B or T-80.

From late in 1962 the basic M60 was replaced in production by the more advanced M60A1. Although this was a distinct advance on the original it was still far from adequate. Basic improvements had to be incorporated to the gun, engine and suspension to give the tank any degree of parity with its sequels currently in operation with the principle NATO armies. These

***Left: The Israeli army has over 1,000 M60s, now fitted with Blazer reactive armour panels and extra machine guns to suppress infantry anti-tank weapons.***

***Above: The M60 is the highest Main Battle Tank in the world and the commander has a cupola so large it has been used on M113 APCs as a turret.***

***Left: Great hopes were pinned on the M60A2 armed with the Shillelagh 152mm gun/missile system, but in service it was a humiliating failure. All 526 M60A2s were returned for conversion to engineering vehicles.***

***Above: An M60 rumbles through Bavarian woodland on exercise. US armoured units in Germany are stationed in poor tank country where tank combat would be at short range and 'quick draw' encounters would be common.***

were eventually incorporated into the M60A3 variant, which now forms the mainstay of today's United States armoured fleet.

The turret and hull remain of all-cast construction with the Continental AVDS-1790-2A RISE (Reliability Improved Selected Equipment) 12-cylinder diesel engine, capable of developing 750bhp at 2,400rpm and giving a top road speed of 48km/h, situated in a large sloping compartment to the rear. The transmission, co-located with the engine, has one reverse and two forward ranges.

The original torsion-bar suspension, with its six road wheels, idler at the front and drive sprocket at the rear, has been enhanced by the introduction of a tube over the bar-suspension on the first, second and sixth road wheels, whilst the new much improved T142 track, with removeable pads, greatly improves front-line maintenance as well as cross country performance.

The main armament still consists of the old 105-mm M68 gun, but now

***Better American engineering makes the M60 far more reliable than its contemporary Soviet rival, the T-62, and an engine change is far quicker. Later production M60A3s are fitted with a smoke-generating system similar to that of Soviet tanks, which creates a smokescreen by spraying fuel into the exhaust manifold.***

with full stabilisation in elevation and traverse to facilitate firing on the move. The turret, which can traverse through 360° in 15 seconds and allow barrel elevation of +20° and depression of −10°, is fitted with an electro-hydraulic control system capable of manual override in an emergency. The barrel is provided with a large and ungainly, but effective, bore evacuator to keep fumes in the turret to a minimum and a thermal sleeve to ensure constant performance under all-weather conditions.

## *Mixed rounds*

The average rate of fire is stated to be between six and eight rounds per minute. Sixty-three mixed rounds are carried: 26 to the left and right of the driver, 21 in the turret bustle, three under the gun, and 13 immediately available for ready use. It is easy to see that the effect of an enemy projectile penetrating any part of the turret or forward chassis would be devastating for the entire crew!

A variety of ammunition, effective to a maximum range of 2,000 metres, is available, including APDS-T (Armour Piercing Discarding Sabot-Tracer), HEAT-T (High Explosive Anti Tank-Tracer), and Smoke WP-T (White Phosphorus-Tracer).

A 7.62-mm M73 machine-gun is mounted coaxially with the main armament, whilst limited localized protection is provided by a 0.5-in M85 machine-gun mounted on the commander's cupola. 5,950 rounds of 7.62-mm and 900 rounds of 0.5-in ammunition are carried.

Engine smoke dischargers supported by small dischargers on each side of the turret are now fitted to all models, as is a comprehensive NBC and top loading air filtration system, passive night vision devices and passive searchlight over the main armament.

## *Variants*

Both an AVLB (Armoured Vehicle Launched Bridge) and CEV (Combat Engineer Vehicle) are available. The AVLB consists of a standard chassis with an hydraulic cylinder assembly, and a scissors bridge capable of carrying any NATO tank and of spanning a width of 18.288 metres replaces the turret.

The CEV, which first entered service in 1968, is based on a modified M60A1 chassis. Armed with a 165-mm M135 demolition gun capable of firing an M123A1 HEP (High Explosive Plastic) round, a 7.62-mm coaxial machine-gun and 0.5-in machine-gun above the commander's cupola, the CEV is also fitted with an 'A' frame mounted at the front of the hull, an hydraulically-operated dozer

# Inside the M60

The M60 is bigger and heavier than any post-war Soviet tank but carries a smaller calibre armament than any Russian MBT since the T-55. On the other hand, better engineering makes it more reliable than some of its potential opponents and superior fire control helps give it the edge in 'quick draw' situations.

**Commander's cupola**
The large cupola increases the height of the tank, giving the commander a good view but, in the Israeli Army's opinion, making too big a target. The cupola traverses independently and is armed with a .50 calibre machine gun.
**Loader**
He has his own hatch to the left of the commander's cupola and an M37 periscope with 360° traverse. Thirteen 105 mm shells are stored in the turret for immediate use, 26 in the forward part of the hull and 21 in the turret bustle.
**Driver**
The driver has a single piece hatch cover that swings open to the right. Like most tank drivers he can be trapped in his seat if the gun is stuck above his hatch but, unlike most, he has an escape hatch in the hull floor for emergencies.
**Frontal armour**
The armoured glacis of the M60 is protected by 225 mm of armour plate, which is comparable to the armour of a T-72 and over twice as well protected as the T-62.

***The M60 carries more than twice the armour thickness of the T-62. The 105-mm gun is perfectly capable of knocking out early model T-72s as the Israelis demonstrated in Lebanon during 1982, but it will need improved ammunition to cope with the more heavily armoured T-64.***

Ballistic shaped turret
The M60A1 introduced this more angular shaped turret, better able to deflect a shell striking the turret from the front. Armour thickness is 250 mm at the front and 138 mm on the sides.
Infra red/white light searchlight
Can project a narrow or broad beam of light and can sharply increase its light intensity for up to 20 seconds.
M68 105 mm gun
This is the British L7 105 mm barrel fixed to a drop-block breech mechanism. An experienced crew can fire up to eight aimed rounds a minute, much faster than the 115 mm gun on the Soviet T-62.
Gunner
The M60A3 has a laser range finder and solid state computer replacing the optical range finder and mechanical fire control system of the M60A1. Range, target and other data is fed to the computer, which then lays the gun accordingly.
Smoke generation
In addition to the usual smoke created by labouring diesel engines, M60s are now fitted with an engine exhaust system, allowing them to create a smokescreen by spraying fuel on to the engine manifold in a similar manner to Soviet vehicles.
Suspension
The torsion bar suspension system consists of rubber tyred road wheels with a drive sprocket at the rear and return track rollers. The M60 can ford 1.2 metres without preparation and twice as deep if it is prepared.

blade, and a two-speed winch with a capacity of 11,340 kg mounted on the rear. The CEV is now employed by combat engineer battalions to destroy enemy fortifications, fill in trenches, remove obstacles and build defensive emplacements.

## The future

At present the M60 and M60A3 are in service with countries as diverse as Austria, Ethiopia, Iran, Italy, Jordan and, of course, the United States. By 1984 just under 15,000 M60s had been produced and various updating kits, notably the General Products Division Teledyne Continental Motors system, will take this ageing MBT well into the next century.

In a series of searing attacks made during the US National Guard Adjutant Generals' Conference held earlier this year, serious shortcomings were identified in the M60A3 TTS (Thermal Sight) tank, and plans were mooted to introduce an updated M60A4. Mobility deficiencies in the suspension and powerpack resulting in a lack of power, marginal control at high speed, and inefficient stiff transmission were highlighted. The high-

***The M60's lofty height would be an embarrassment on a completely flat plain, but billiard-table terrain is rare. Able to depress its gun 10°, the M60 is better able to take up hull-down positions in undulating ground than the much smaller Soviet tanks.***

vehicle profile, virtually useless cupola, poor NBC protection, minimal armour and fire-control deficiencies were also criticised.

### Improvements

A number of improvements were suggested varying from the introduction of appliqué armour, the retrofitting of a new 120-mm main gun, and the installation of the AVDS 1790 diesel engine rated at 1,050 hp. It is estimated that updating would cost

***The M60's massive bulk only becomes obvious when you stand next to it. Unlike the Soviets, the Americans do not ruthlessly subordinate crew comfort to tactical advantage.***

# Battlefield Evaluation: comparing

## M60

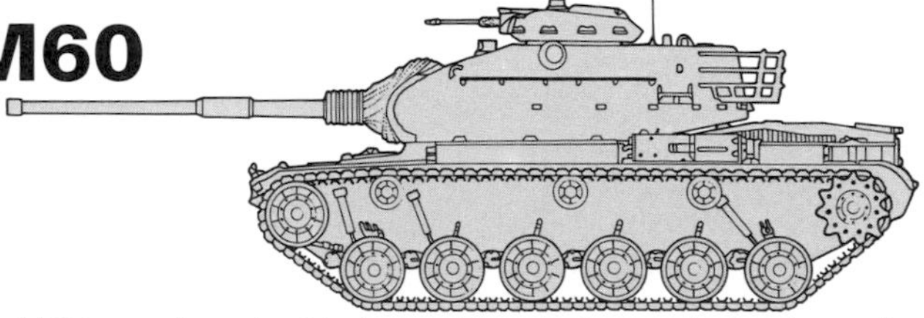

The M60 has performed well in the Israeli army and was undoubtedly superior to its contemporary Soviet rivals, the T-55 and T-62, but the last M60s coming off the production line in August 1987 face much more capable opponents in the shape of the T-64, T-72 and T-80. Against these the M60 is undergunned, underpowered and uncomfortably large. New ammunition for the 105-mm gun may be part of the answer, but unless a comprehensive modernisation programme is undertaken the M60 will not be able to meet Soviet MBTs on equal terms.

**Specification:**
**Crew:** 4
**Combat weight:** 52 tonnes
**Road speed:** 48 km/h
**Power-to-weight ratio:** 14 hp/tonne
**Length:** 6.9 m
**Height:** 3.27 m
**Armament:** 1×105-mm gun; 1×12.7-mm machine-gun; 1×7.62-mm machine-gun

**Assessment**

| | |
|---|---|
| **Firepower** | **** |
| **Protection** | **** |
| **Age** | **** |
| **Worldwide users** | *** |

***The M60 was an uninspired design, superior to older Soviet tanks thanks to better engineering.***

## M48

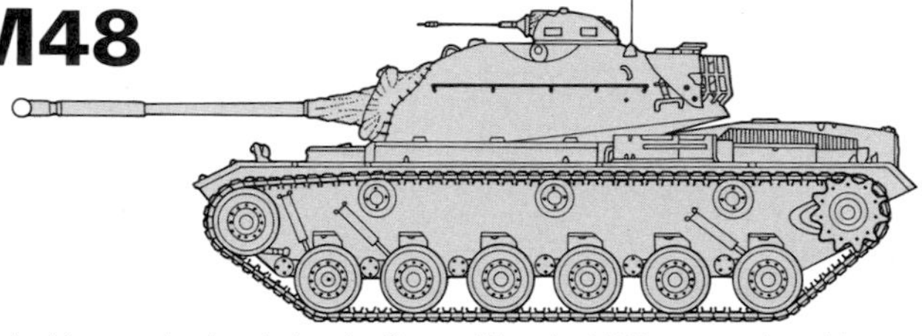

Rushed into production during the Korean War, the M48 was produced between 1952 and 1959 and demonstrated that US tank design had a lot to learn from the Soviet Union in terms of firepower, protection and ballistic shape. The basic design was followed by seven variants, each more capable than the last; Israeli M48s in particular were soon made into effective MBTs. Many remain in service around the world, a mediocre vehicle turned into a powerful tank by the addition of a 105-mm gun and modern fire control systems.

**Specification:** (M48A2)
**Crew:** 4
**Combat weight:** 47 tonnes
**Road speed:** 48 km/h
**Power-to-weight ratio:** 17 hp/tonne
**Length:** 6.8 m
**Height:** 3.1 m
**Armament:** 1×90-mm gun; 1×7.62-mm machine-gun; 1×12.7-mm machine-gun

**Assessment**

| | |
|---|---|
| **Firepower** | *** |
| **Protection** | ** |
| **Age** | ***** |
| **Worldwide users** | *** |

***Inferior to contemporary Soviet MBTs, the M48 was the mainstay of US armour deployed to Vietnam.***

## T-54/55

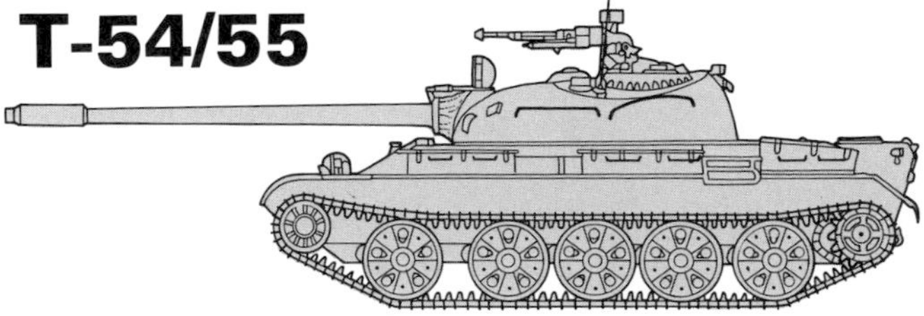

The T-54/55 series of Main Battle Tanks has seen more action than any other post-war tank, and it is estimated that over 100,000 were built. Low readiness Soviet formations still use them; they remain popular in the Warsaw Pact, and no Soviet-equipped army in Africa or the Middle East is complete without a number of T-55s rumbling through the capital. T-54/55s are uncomfortable, exhausting to drive and have an inaccurate gun. On the other hand they are light but very tough, present a low target, and are easy to maintain.

**Specification:** (T-55)
**Crew:** 4
**Combat weight:** 36 tonnes
**Road speed:** 50 km/h
**Power-to-weight ratio:** 16 hp/tonne
**Length:** 6.45 m
**Height:** 2.4 m
**Armament:** 1×100-mm gun; 2×7.62-mm machine-guns; 1×12.7-mm machine-gun

**Assessment**

| | |
|---|---|
| **Firepower** | ** |
| **Protection** | *** |
| **Age** | ***** |
| **Worldwide users** | ***** |

***The most widely-manufactured tank since World War II, the T-54/55 is crude but soldier-proof.***

$730,000 per tank, and finance will clearly play a large part in deciding whether or not this ambitious plan proceeds. If the National Guard gets its way, and a projected 420 vehicles a year are refitted, the entire conversion programme will be completed by 1997. By then it is more than likely that the Abrams will have displaced the M60 series completely from front line units. In August 1987, the last M60s were being completed and the production line is empty.

***An M60 swings its 105-mm gun to engage a target on the move, an ability notably lacking in the T-62. Faster turret traverse and superior fire control gives the M60 greater tactical flexibility.***

# the M-60 with its rivals

## T-62

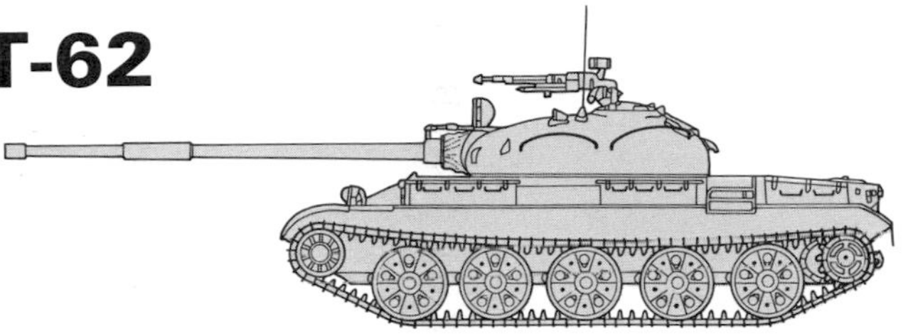

Standard equipment of Soviet tank units during the 1970s but now replaced by the T-64, T-72 and T-80 in first-line formations, the T-62 is inferior to the M60 in fire control and human engineering. The smoothbore gun is accurate at up to 1,500 metres and the combination of well-sloped armour and the usual Soviet low silhouette gives it adequate protection. On the other hand, the gun's accuracy deteriorates quickly and its rate of fire is low by comparison with NATO MBTs.

**Specification:**
**Crew:** 4
**Combat weight:** 40 tonnes
**Road speed:** 50 km/h
**Power-to-weight ratio:** 14.5 hp/tonne
**Length:** 6.63 m
**Height:** 2.4 m
**Armament:** 1×115-mm gun; 1×7.62-mm machine-gun; 1×12.7-mm machine-gun

**Assessment**

| | |
|---|---|
| **Firepower** | *** |
| **Protection** | *** |
| **Age** | ***** |
| **Worldwide users** | ***** |

***Despite its excellent silhouette and powerful armament, the T-62 has several major weaknesses as an MBT.***

## Chieftain

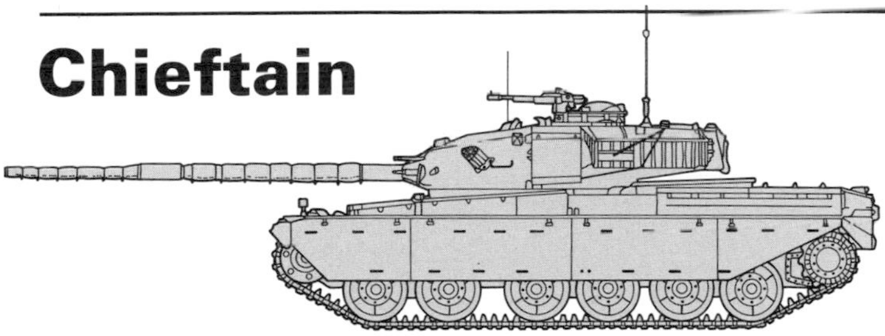

A few years after Soviet tank formations received their T-62s the British Army received the Chieftain, which was substantially superior and undoubtedly the best tank produced in the 1960s. The 120-mm gun could knock out any rival tank, its armour protection was better than the M60, and it remains superior to the American tank in most respects. Its only major weakness was its powerpack, which scandalously let down a magnificent combat vehicle.

**Specification:**
**Crew:** 4
**Combat weight:** 54 tonnes
**Road speed:** 48 km/h
**Power-to-weight ratio:** 13.5 hp/tonne
**Length:** 7.52 m
**Height:** 2.9 m
**Armament:** 1×120-mm gun; 2×7.62-mm machine-guns

**Assessment**

| | |
|---|---|
| **Firepower** | ***** |
| **Protection** | ***** |
| **Age** | ***** |
| **Worldwide users** | ** |

***The Chieftain's design was more thoroughly prepared than that of the M60, and the result was a better tank.***

## Leopard 1

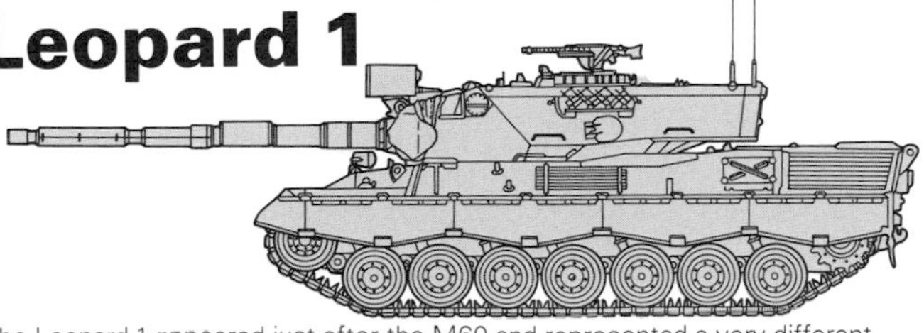

The Leopard 1 appeared just after the M60 and represented a very different approach to MBT design: less armour protection made it substantially faster and gave it a power-to-weight ratio second to none. Armed with the same British-designed 105-mm gun as the later M48s and M60, the Leopard had speed and firepower but no capacity to absorb damage. Like the M60 it is a far more comfortable vehicle to fight in than the T-55 or T-62, and it has proved a popular vehicle for export.

**Specification:**
**Crew:** 4
**Combat weight:** 36 tonnes
**Road speed:** 65 km/h
**Power-to-weight ratio:** 20.75 hp/tonne
**Length:** 7.09 m
**Height:** 2.6 m
**Armament:** 1×105-mm gun; 2×7.62-mm machine-guns

**Assessment**

| | |
|---|---|
| **Firepower** | **** |
| **Protection** | ** |
| **Age** | ***** |
| **Worldwide users** | *** |

***The Leopard is a radically different vehicle from the M60, trading armour protection for greater mobility.***

# Weapons and Equipment Guide No. 13

# Fighting with the GPMG

***The General Purpose Machine Gun used by the British Army is a development of the Belgian FN MAG, the most successful post-World War II machine-gun.*** Over 200,000 have been made and about 75 different armies have adopted it. It is a tough, straightforward weapon, light enough to be carried by one man, but it can be tripod-mounted and used to deliver sustained fire.

***The GPMG provides most of the firepower of an infantry section. Here the gunner concentrates on firing short bursts on the target while his assistant ensures that the belt is feeding into the gun properly.***

When it was introduced into British service it replaced two weapons: the heavy, water-cooled Vickers gun that had been in use since before World War I, and the famous Bren gun that British troops found so effective during World War II.

### Fire and movement

For the last 50 years infantry tactics have been built around the firepower and movement of the individual section, which is between eight and 13 men strong, depending on the army.

Two or three men are the gun group, and the rest are the rifle group. The gun group lays down covering fire with a light machine-gun on a bipod, to keep the enemies' heads down while the rifle group advances. The rifle group then lays down fire so that the gun group can advance; in this manner the section leapfrogs forward to assault the enemy. This technique was used very successfully during the Falklands campaign to take Argentine positions.

***The GPMG is fired in short bursts of between three and five rounds so that the rate of fire is about 25 rounds a minute. If rapid fire is ordered the rate is stepped up to about 100 rounds per minute, but sustained firing at such a rate will overheat the barrel and exhaust the sections' ammunition.***

## Enemy suppression

The other main role of the machine-gun is to fire continuously to suppress enemy positions or dominate areas of ground with a hail of bullets. This SF (Sustained Fire) role was traditionally left to heavy, tripod-mounted weapons, which were usually cooled by a continuous flow of water in a casing around the barrel.

During World War II, the Germans developed a machine-gun, the MG42, that was able to fulfil both roles. When mounted on a bipod it was excellent in the light role; and, thanks to clever design and an easy-to-change barrel, it could be mounted on a tripod, fitted with special sights and successfully used in the Sustained Fire role. The general-purpose machine-gun was born.

## Single weapon

The idea of a GPMG was very attractive. Soldiers needed to learn the workings of only one weapon, and only one set of spares needed to be produced. After the war, numerous designs appeared; the FN, forerunner of the GPMG, was the best.

## SBS assault

In the Falklands war the Royal Marines Special Boat Squadron relied heavily on the GPMG, especially during the landings at San Carlos Water. 'S' section and some attached commandos, about 40 men in total, attacked an Argentine position on Fanning Head with 16 GPMGs between them. They fired predominantly tracer rounds to give the impression that a

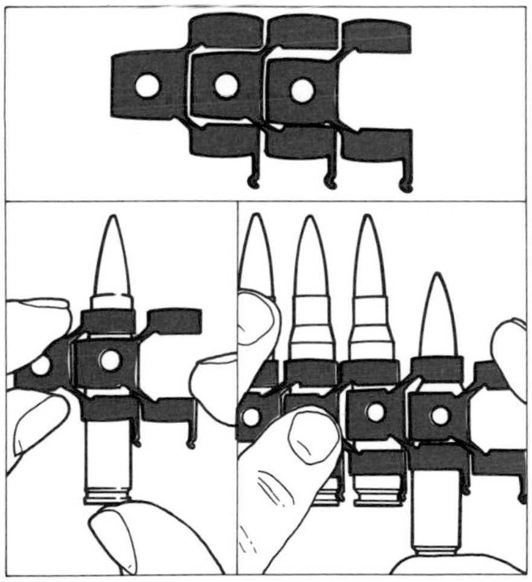

***Ammunition for the GPMG is usually supplied in a 200-round belt with one tracer round set between every three normal ball rounds. However, some elite units prefer to put together their own 'cocktail' belts of tracer, ball, armour-piercing or other ammo. Belts can easily be joined together, as shown above.***

***Machine-gunners must learn to clear a stoppage very quickly: cock the gun, lower the butt and open the top cover. Clear the feed tray, raise the butt and pull the trigger, then reload.***

***Ammunition stacked and ready, both men of the machine-gun team scan the front for targets. The No. 2's job is to ensure a continuous supply of ammunition.***

***The non-regulation 'Mexican bandit' method of carrying an ammo belt. The problem with being good with a GPMG in training is that you get to carry it.***

***A GPMG lies surrounded by empty shell cases and the links from the belt. The gas regulator has blown off after some lengthy bursts of fire, rendering the weapon useless. The regulator must be carefully adjusted to control the rate of fire.***

***Longer bursts of about 10 rounds are used against long range-targets. Really long bursts are reserved for an enemy assault, or against armour where machine-gun fire is used to destroy optical devices and sighting equipment.***

# Inside the GPMG

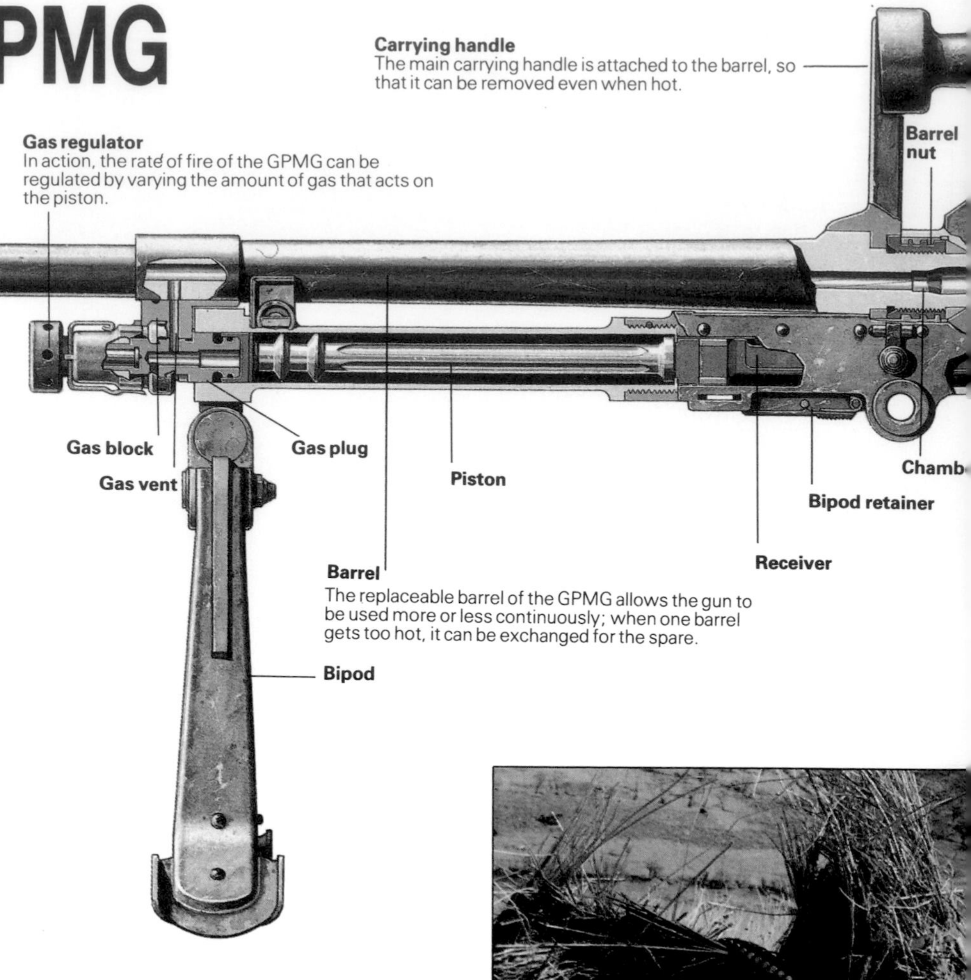

Carrying handle
The main carrying handle is attached to the barrel, so that it can be removed even when hot.
Flash hider
Foresight
Gas regulator
In action, the rate of fire of the GPMG can be regulated by varying the amount of gas that acts on the piston.
Barrel nut
Gas block
Gas plug
Gas vent
Piston
Chamb
Bipod retainer
Receiver
Barrel
The replaceable barrel of the GPMG allows the gun to be used more or less continuously; when one barrel gets too hot, it can be exchanged for the spare.
Bipod

Light in weight and easy to carry, strongly and simply constructed, easy to strip and maintain, and firing the slightly heavier 7.62-mm NATO round, the General Purpose Machine Gun has for many years been the British Army's first-line automatic support weapon.

unit of at least battalion strength was assaulting the position, and bluffed the enemy into submission!

### *Firing from the hip*

In close-quarter battle a belt of only 50 rounds will normally be used, and often the gunner will use an old '44-pattern water-bottle pouch as a feed-bag to the right of the GPMG field tray. As he advances with a sling across his back and shoulders, he can fire the weapon from the hip at any target that presents itself.

This method was used on 19 July 1972 during the Battle of Mirbat in Oman when a force of 80 members of 'G' squadron, 22 SAS, rushed to the rescue of an eight-man SAS training team that had been attacked by 250 Arab Communist guerrillas. Nearly every third man in the relief force carried a GPMG.

### *Tripod mounting*

For employment in the Sustained Fire role, the GPMG is mounted to a tripod. This is a spring-buffered assembly, and the gun is simply dropped into its cradle and held there by two pins so that once locked in place it is able to recoil for a short distance, the spring buffers absorbing the shock.

In the British Army the GPMG in each section is being replaced by a pair of Light Support Weapons and the section is being reorganised into two four-man groups, each with one LSW and three SA80s. The GPMGs will be grouped together and used in the SF role, rather like the old Vickers guns.

By using several machine-guns together, a large area of ground can be swept with bullets, making it impossible for enemy infantry to move across. Placed on the flanks of a defensive position, GPMGs will be used to cover the ground in front of British trenches.

***The GPMG's integral bipod makes it very accurate indeed, especially when used from the prone position.***

## Basic GPMG strip

**1** Open the top cover, cock the gun and lift the feed tray. Check that the chamber and body are clear, lower the feed tray and close the top cover. Then hold the cocking handle and press the trigger, allowing the working parts to go forward under control.

**2** Holding the receiver in the left hand, grip the butt with the right. Use the forefinger of the right hand to press up the butt catch, and slide the butt upwards and clear of the body.

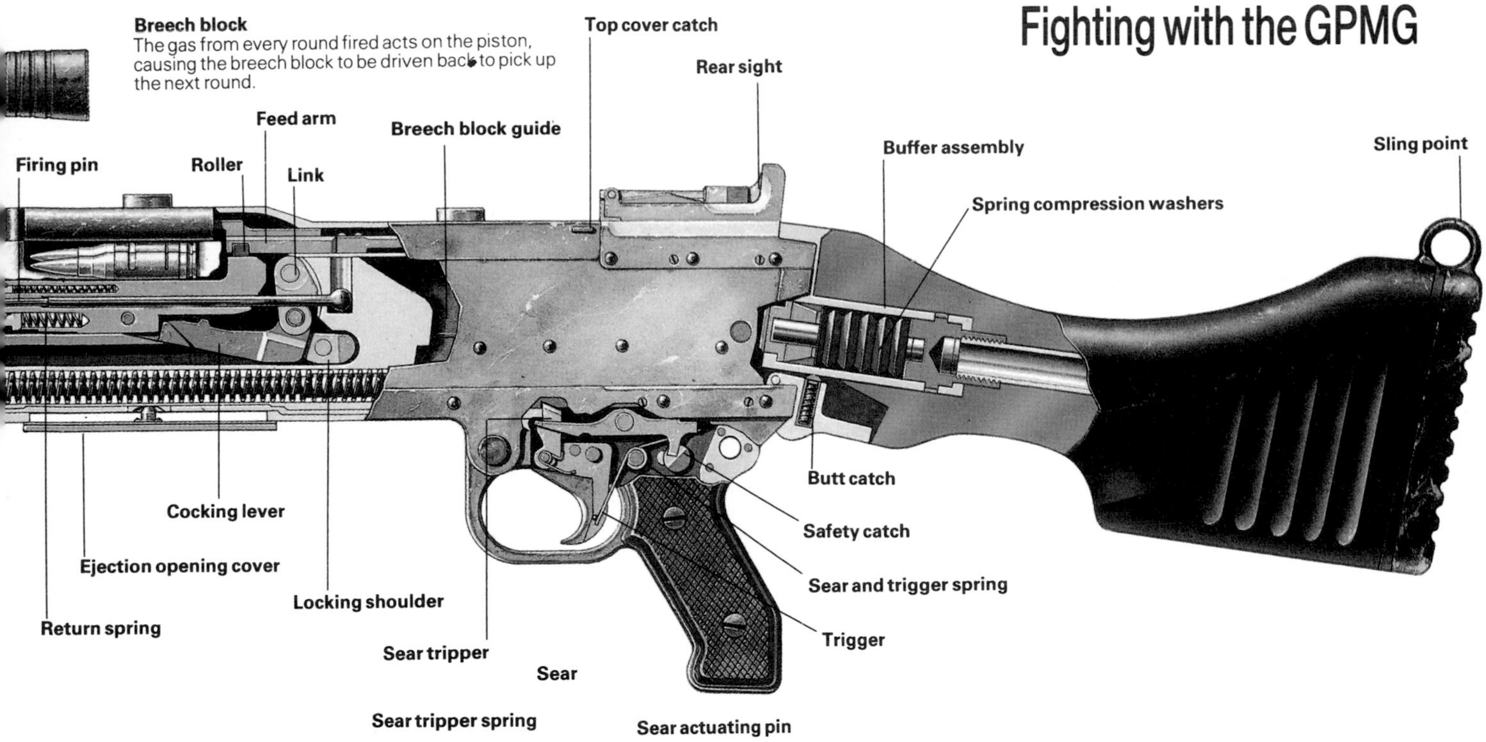


# The gas regulator

The GPMG is gas-operated; as the bullet approaches the end of the barrel, some of the gas propelling it is diverted downwards, where it pushes a piston back. This opens the bolt, ejects the spent cartridge case and completes the action.

By rotating the ring on the gas regulator, the amount of gas tapped from the barrel can be adjusted, thus controlling the rate of fire of the weapon.

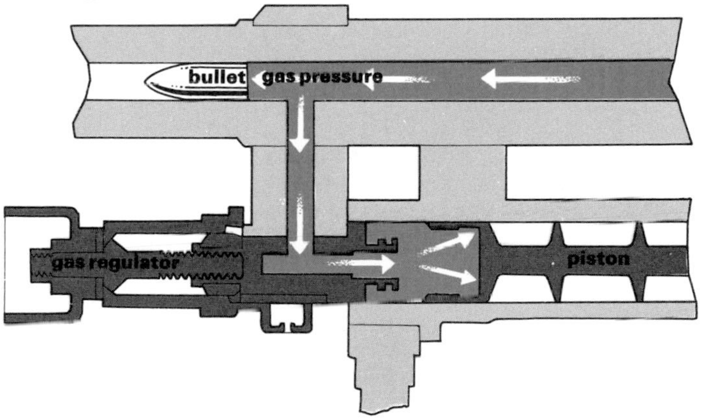

**3** The return spring rod is held in place by means of a keyhole-shaped slot. Disengage the return spring rod with a forward and upward movement by pressing on the back with the right thumb. Withdraw it to the rear.

**4** Place the palm of the left hand behind the body of the gun, and then pull back sharply on the cocking handle with the right hand. The piston and breech block will now protrude from the body and can be withdrawn.

**5** Pressing down on the insulated barrel-locking catch with the thumb of the left hand, grip the carrying handle with the right hand and turn it to the vertical position. The barrel can now be pushed forward and lifted clear.

## The ammunition feed mechanism

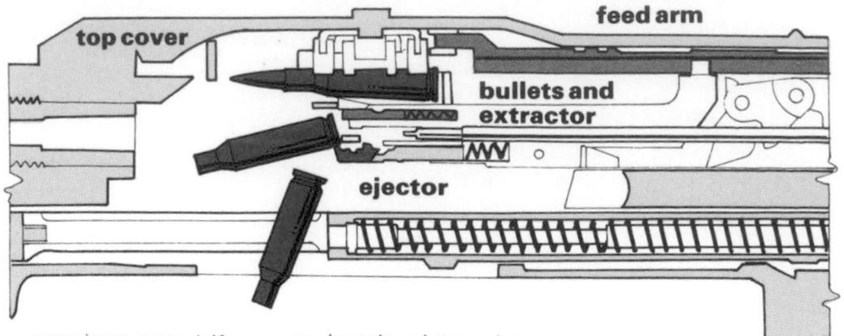


As the gas piston is driven backwards by some of the gas propelling the bullet, the breech block is unlocked and moves backwards. The extractor withdraws the empty cartridge case from the chamber and the ejector forces it out of the gun via the ejection slot.

The working parts continue to move back, compressing the return spring, and are finally halted by the buffer unit. If the trigger remains pressed, if fresh rounds are in the belt and if the gas regulator is allowing enough gas pressure against the piston, the working parts will rebound from the buffer and the GPMG will continue to fire.

### Multi-purpose

Although it is leaving the infantry sections, the GPMG remains a multi-purpose weapon. Main Battle Tanks use a modified version, in which the belt can be loaded without lifting the top cover, which would be awkward in the cramped interior of a tank turret. This version also vents all gases through the barrel and thus outside the vehicle, rather than from the gas regulator; otherwise the tank would quickly fill with fumes.

The GPMG continues to serve in the air defence role. The ships of the British Task Force in San Carlos fairly bristled with GPMGs pointing sky-

# Battlefield Evaluation: comparing

## L7A2 General Purpose Machine-Gun

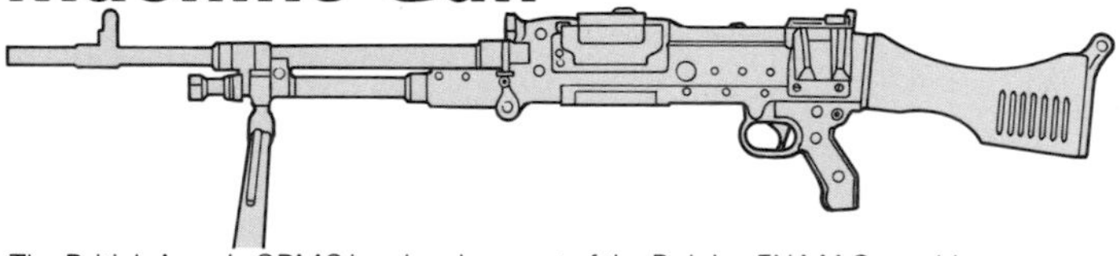

The British Army's GPMG is a development of the Belgian FN MAG machine-gun, and has been used for about 30 years to equip the gun group in each infantry section. It is an air-cooled weapon, so it overheats more quickly than the old water-cooled Vickers guns and cannot maintain its theoretical maximum rate of fire. It tends to pull forward when firing from a bipod, so the butt must be pulled firmly against the shoulder and held there with the left hand.

**Specification:**
**Cartridge:** 7.62 mm NATO
**Weight:** 10.9 kg
**Length:** 1232 mm
**Cyclic rate of fire:** 750-1000 rounds per minute
**Effective range:** 1200 m

**Assessment**
**Reliability** ***
**Accuracy** ****
**Age** ****
**Worldwide users** ****

***The GPMG in each British infantry section is being replaced by a pair of Light Support Weapons.***

## 7.62 mm M60 GPMG

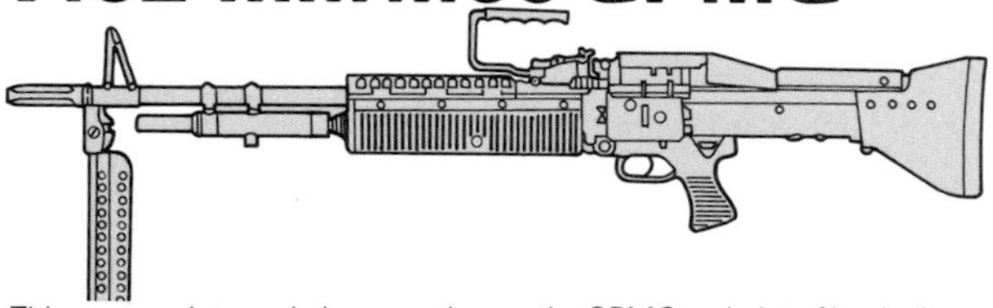

This appeared at much the same time as the GPMG and a lot of its design, notably the belt feed, was copied from the German MG42. Gas-operated, it uses a rotating bolt which locks into the rear of the barrel. There is no gas adjustment; the system is self-regulating in that once sufficient gas has gone into the piston to move it, the gas supply is then cut off. It is belt-fed and fires at the relatively slow rate of 550 rpm. The M60 is used by the USA, and also by Australia and some Far Eastern countries.

**Specification:**
**Cartridge:** 7.62 mm × 51
**Weight:** 10.5 kg
**Length:** 1105 mm
**Cyclic rate of fire:** 550 rounds per minute
**Effective range:** 1000 m

**Assessment**
**Reliability** ***
**Accuracy** ***
**Age** ***
**Worldwide users** ***

***Known for a variety of reasons as 'the Pig', the M60 still equips US infantry squads.***

## 7.62 mm PK GPMG

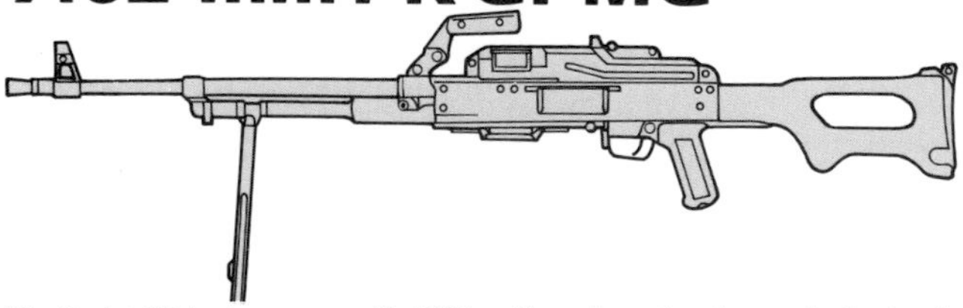

The Soviet PK design appeared in 1964 and is perhaps the closest the Soviets have come to the GPMG idea. The family consists of a number of weapons for various applications, but the basic infantry gun is the PK or PKS; the former has a bipod and the latter tripod mounting attachments. This gun is the standard infantry support machine-gun throughout the Warsaw Pact countries and will also be found in armies supplied by the USSR.

**Specification:**
**Cartridge:** 7.62 mm × 54R
**Weight:** 19 kg
**Length:** 1160 mm
**Cyclic rate of fire:** 690-720 rounds per minute
**Effective range:** 1000 m

**Assessment**
**Reliability** ****
**Accuracy** ***
**Age** ***
**Worldwide users** ****

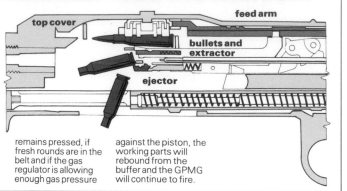

***This stack of PK machine-guns was found in a warehouse by US troops during the invasion of Grenada.***

wards, and while the chance of a single machine-gun bringing down a fast jet is pretty remote, massed machine-gun fire is an offputting prospect for most pilots. Also during the Falklands war, GPMGs were fitted to many of the utility helicopters, where they were used by crewmen acting as door gunners.

***Because the GPMG tends to pull forward, it is a common mistake to pull the butt into your shoulder. This can disturb your aim: what you should do is to move your body up to the gun and keep the right shoulder completely still while firing.***

# the GPMG with its rivals

## 7.62 mm RPK light machine-gun

The RPK is a light machine-gun rather than a general purpose-weapon; it fires from magazines, not belts, and its barrel cannot be changed. Like the British Light Support Weapon, it provides each infantry section with long-range, accurate firepower, but cannot deliver the great weight of fire necessary for the SF (Sustained Fire) role. Introduced 20 years ago, it equips all Soviet and Warsaw Pact forces and many guerrilla armies throughout the world.

**Specification:**
**Cartridge:** 7.62 mm × 39
**Weight:** 6 kg (including 40 round mag)
**Length:** 1035 mm
**Cyclic rate of fire:** 600 rounds per minute
**Effective range:** 750 m

**Assessment**
- **Reliability** *****
- **Accuracy** ***
- **Age** ****
- **Worldwide users** ****

***An Iraqi machine-gunner takes aim with an RPK, the heavy-barrelled version of the AKM assault rifle.***

## 7.62-mm Bren gun

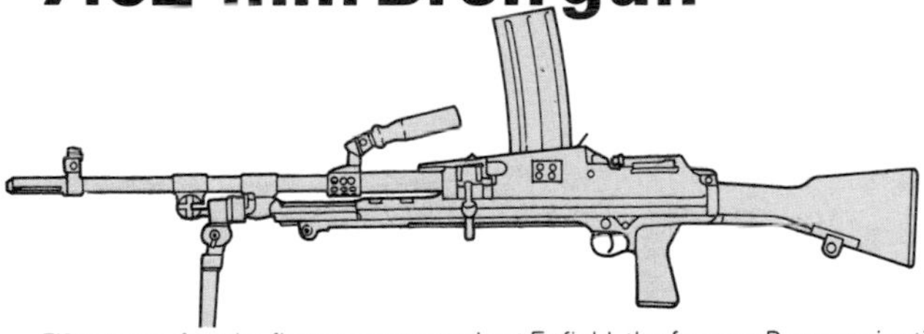

Fifty years after the first one was made at Enfield, the famous Bren gun is still in limited service with the British Army. The original Bren guns served as section light machine-guns with Vickers guns providing the sustained fire role when both weapons were replaced by the GPMG. The arrival of the Light Support Weapon will finally remove the Bren from front-line service.

**Specification:**
**Cartridge:** 7.62 mm × 51
**Weight:** 9.53 kg
**Length:** 1133 mm
**Cyclic rate of fire:** 500 rounds per minute
**Effective range:** 600 m

**Assessment**
- **Reliability** ***
- **Accuracy** ****
- **Age** *****
- **Worldwide users** ***

***An L4A4 7.62-mm Bren gun is carried on a patrol in South Armagh, Northern Ireland.***

## 7.62-mm HK21 Heckler & Koch GPMG

The HK21 is a belt-fed general-purpose machine-gun which, by the addition of an adaptor, can fire any of the magazines used by H & K's G3 assault rifle. Closely based on the G3, the HK21 is able to fire single shots as well as fully automatic. Changing the barrel is a fast and easy process and a great help when firing in the SF role. A recoil booster allows the weapon to be used normally while firing blank cartridges, which is a useful training aid.

**Specification:**
**Cartridge:** 7.62 mm × 51
**Weight:** 7.3 kg
**Length:** 1021 mm
**Cyclic rate of fire:** 900 rounds per minute
**Effective range:** 1200 m

**Assessment**
- **Reliability** ****
- **Accuracy** ***
- **Age** ****
- **Worldwide users** *

***Portuguese troops prepare to fire the HK21 GPMG, which is now out of production.***

# HARRIER

## Hell-raiser in Hiding

*Two Harrier GR.Mk 3s bank steeply as they weave through mountainous country, using the terrain to screen them from enemy radar. The 455-litre fuel tanks carried under the wings are stressed for combat manoeuvres.*

***All NATO armies rely heavily on air support, but most aircraft can only operate from conventional airfields. Any airfield can be attacked with bombs, or long-range rockets or persistent nerve gas, temporarily depriving the ground forces of any help from the air.*** However, there is one aircraft that is not tied to a runway; the British Aerospace Harrier can fly and fight from almost anywhere.

If another war in Europe seems imminent, the RAF's two squadrons of Harriers will leave their base at Gütersloh in West Germany, 120 km from the border with East Germany, and deploy into the countryside. Thousands of sites have been pre-surveyed and kept on file, and peacetime exercises often involve a sudden deployment to one of them.

### Hiding in towns

Not all sites are in rural areas: the RAF have found that towns can be even better than forest clearings. Roads and car parks make good take-off and landing areas, and large buildings with adjoining car parks, such as supermarkets, provide cover and concealment against infra-red sensors.

There are other NATO combat aircraft that do not need conventional runways. Some are theoretically able to operate from grass, but they are unable to carry a full weapons load if they do so. Most can take off from a suitable stretch of road, and would make good use of an extensive motorway system.

Take-off from a motorway is no problem. The pilot lines up, psychs up and blasts off. The snag with operating conventional combat aircraft from a road is the landing: you need a great deal of practice and a very long stretch of road.

*One of No. 4 Squadron's Harrier GR.Mk 3s jumps into the air after a short take-off run. The aircraft can take off vertically, but not with a full fuel/weapons load.*

### Wartime deployment

In wartime the Harrier force will deploy to six sites, which will be controlled from a centrally-positioned Forward Wing Operations Centre (FWOC). The sites are established by the Royal Engineers and guarded by detachments from the RAF Regiment using Scorpion light tanks and Spartan APCs. The sites are occupied on a temporary basis, aircraft and personnel moving to new ones to avoid enemy air or artillery attack.

At air shows, the Harrier frequently demonstrates its ability to take off vertically, but the 'jump jet' cannot do this carrying a full load of fuel and weapons. Instead, it takes off like a normal aircraft but uses a very short take-off run of just over 350 metres. (This compares to 700 metres required by a possible foe, the Soviet MiG-27 aircraft.) If no hard surface is available the Harrier needs strips of Pierced Steel Planking (PSP) or wire mesh laid on the ground for it to take off.

*A Harrier of No. 1 Squadron squats in a typical rural hide. Such hides could be located in forest clearings or cut into the edge of a wood.*

## Rural dispersed site

Every farm, woodland clearing or car park can serve as an airfield for Britain's remarkable Harrier. PSP (Pierced Steel Planking) strip can be quickly laid out to form a runway, and camouflage netting serves to obscure the hides from enemy reconnaissance aircraft.

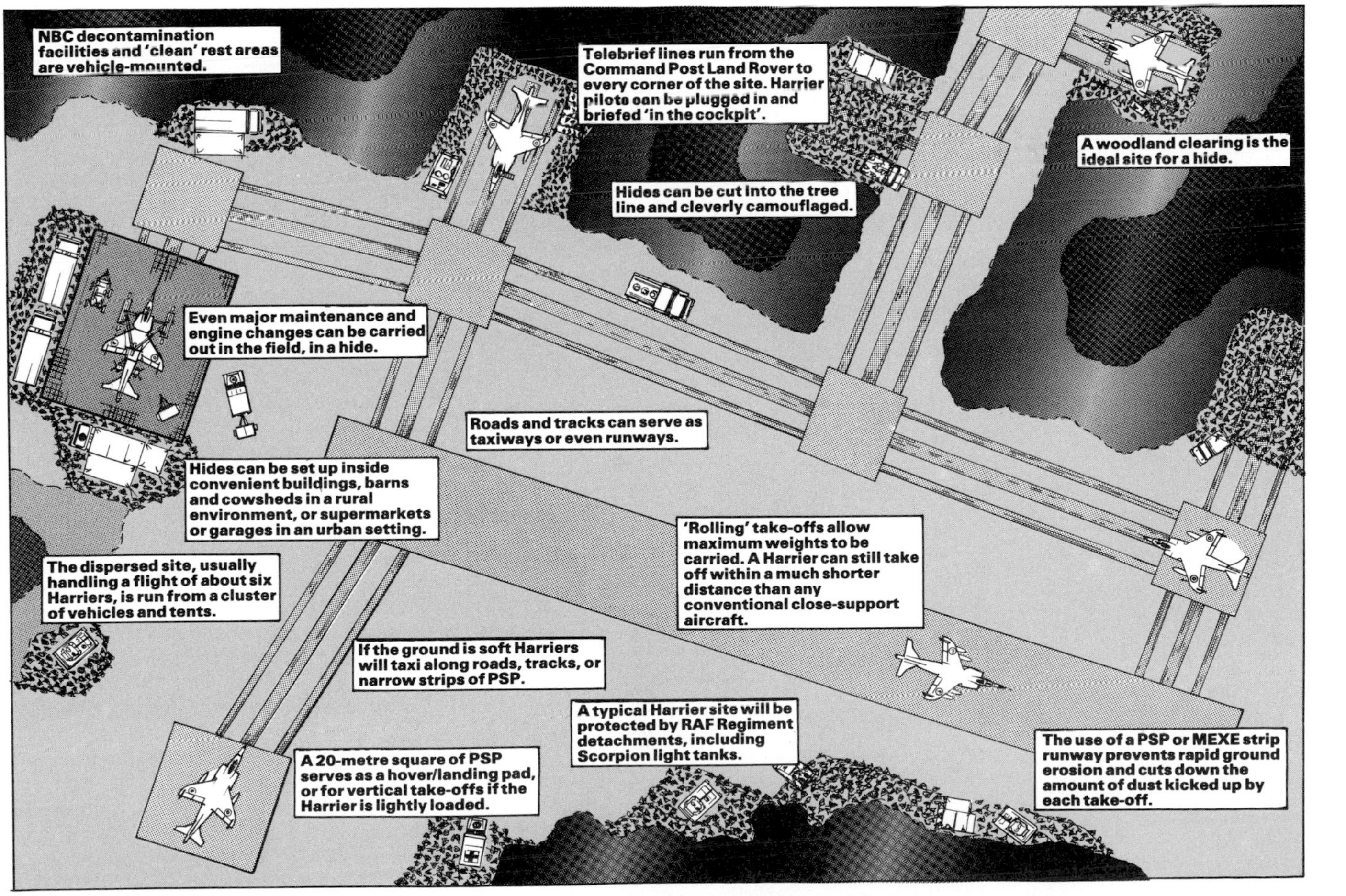

NBC decontamination facilities and 'clean' rest areas are vehicle-mounted.
Telebrief lines run from the Command Post Land Rover to every corner of the site. Harrier pilots can be plugged in and briefed 'in the cockpit'.
A woodland clearing is the ideal site for a hide.
Hides can be cut into the tree line and cleverly camouflaged.
Even major maintenance and engine changes can be carried out in the field, in a hide.
Roads and tracks can serve as taxiways or even runways.
Hides can be set up inside convenient buildings, barns and cowsheds in a rural environment, or supermarkets or garages in an urban setting.
'Rolling' take-offs allow maximum weights to be carried. A Harrier can still take off within a much shorter distance than any conventional close-support aircraft.
The dispersed site, usually handling a flight of about six Harriers, is run from a cluster of vehicles and tents.
If the ground is soft Harriers will taxi along roads, tracks, or narrow strips of PSP.
A typical Harrier site will be protected by RAF Regiment detachments, including Scorpion light tanks.
The use of a PSP or MEXE strip runway prevents rapid ground erosion and cuts down the amount of dust kicked up by each take-off.
A 20-metre square of PSP serves as a hover/landing pad, or for vertical take-offs if the Harrier is lightly loaded.

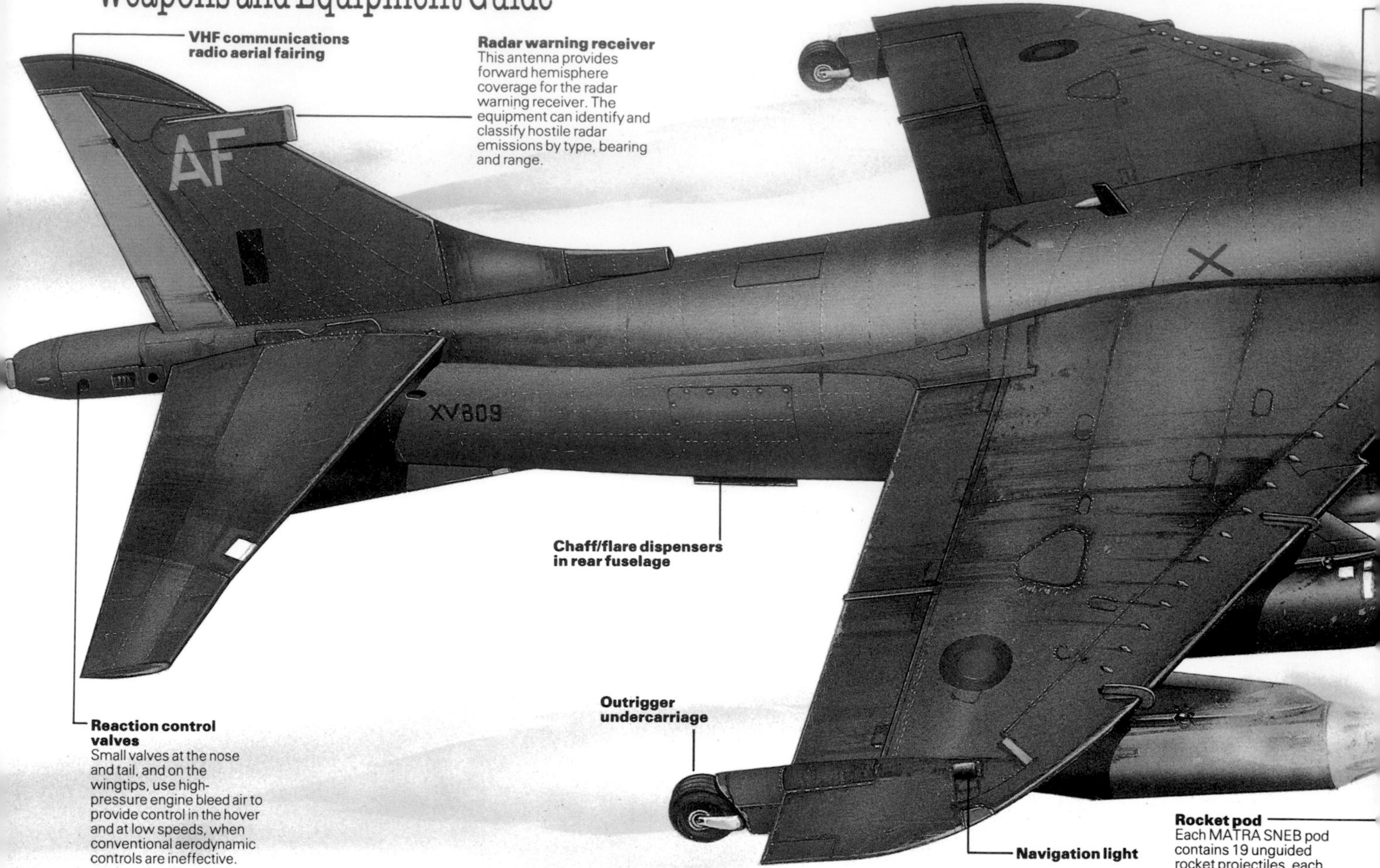

VHF communications radio aerial fairing
Radar warning receiver
This antenna provides forward hemisphere coverage for the radar warning receiver. The equipment can identify and classify hostile radar emissions by type, bearing and range.
AF
XV809
Chaff/flare dispensers in rear fuselage
Outrigger undercarriage
Reaction control valves
Small valves at the nose and tail, and on the wingtips, use high-pressure engine bleed air to provide control in the hover and at low speeds, when conventional aerodynamic controls are ineffective.
Navigation light
Rocket pod
Each MATRA SNEB pod contains 19 unguided rocket projectiles, each with 'flip-out' folding fins and a shaped-charge warhead. The weapons are highly effective against armour.

The Harrier's Rolls-Royce Pegasus turbofan can be started using the aircraft's built-in APU (Auxiliary Power Unit), and the Ferranti INAS (Inertial Navigation and Attack System) can be quickly aligned. The aircraft taxis out of its 'hide' along three narrow metal strips, one for the nose and mainwheels and one for each outrigger.

To make a short or 'rolling-vertical' take-off, the pilot sets a bug on the airspeed indicator to a pre-computed lift-off speed and sets the nozzle angle stop to 50°. He releases the brakes and slams the throttle open, pulling back the nozzle lever to the 50° stop when the ASI needle passes the bug.

## Under way

The vectoring nozzles swivel downwards and the Harrier lifts off. When the aircraft reaches 15 metres in height the pilot retracts the undercarriage and makes the transition to wingborne flight.

The Harrier GR.Mk 3 has a smaller radius of action than most close-support aircraft, but this is usually compensated for by the closer proximity of the Harrier force to the front line and by its ability to sustain a higher sortie rate. The heart of the Harrier lies in its NAVWASS (Navigation and Weapon Aiming Sub System), which allows the Harrier pilot to find and attack his target with great precision.

## Data display

The Ferranti FE 541 Inertial Navigation and Attack System is linked with the Smiths Air Data Computer and Specto-designed HUD (Head-Up Display). Data such as destination and waypoints can be fed into the INAS using a pistol-grip hand controller and fix button mounted on the throttle quadrant.

A projected moving map displays this data, with present aircraft position in the centre. The 35-mm cassette that generates the moving map covers an area of about 800 nautical miles north to south by about 900 nautical miles east to west. The INAS and computer present directions to the pilot on the head-up display and can automatically release weapons, having taken account of aircraft speed, weapon characteristics, wind speed and direction. Alternatively, weapons

## Hunting BL755 Cluster Bomb Unit

The BL755 externally resembles a conventional bomb, but splits open after release and ejects 147 aerodynamically-retarded shaped-charge bomblets with fragmenting warhead casings.

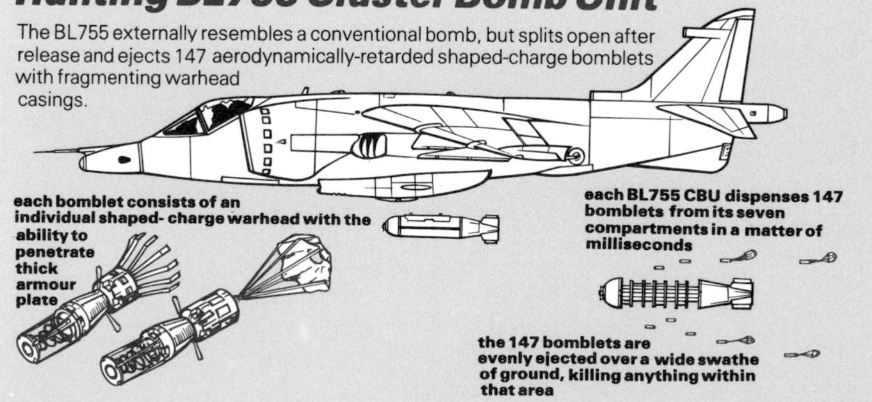

each bomblet consists of an individual shaped- charge warhead with the ability to penetrate thick armour plate
each BL755 CBU dispenses 147 bomblets from its seven compartments in a matter of milliseconds
the 147 bomblets are evenly ejected over a wide swathe of ground, killing anything within that area

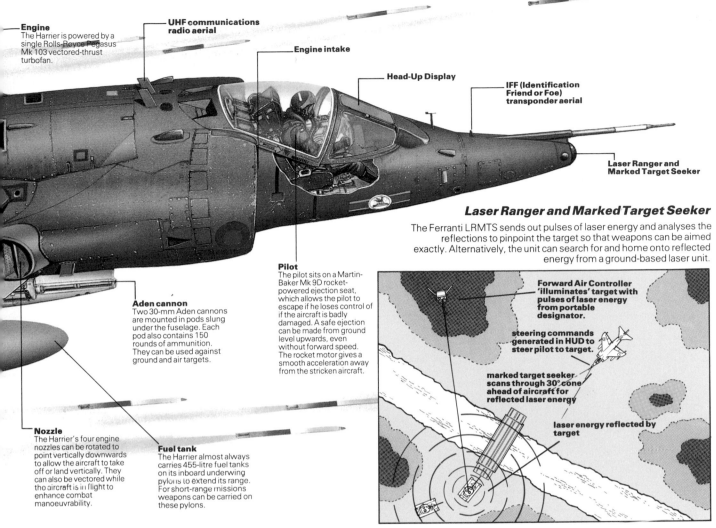

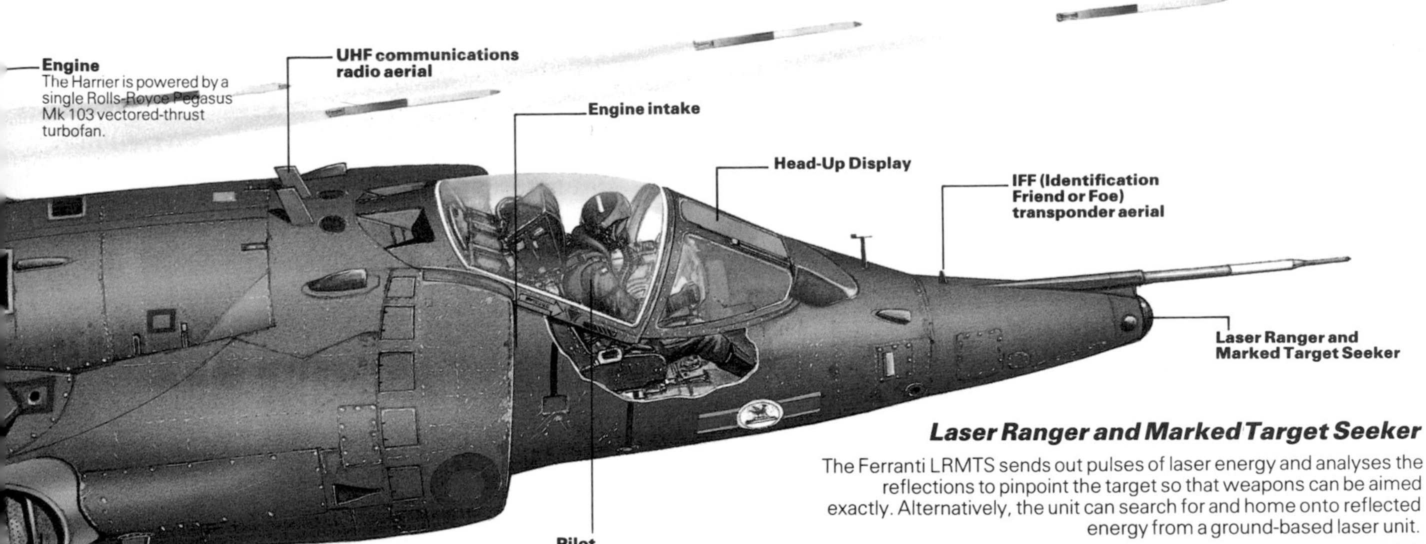
**Engine**
The Harrier is powered by a single Rolls-Royce Pegasus Mk 103 vectored-thrust turbofan.
**UHF communications radio aerial**
**Engine intake**
**Head-Up Display**
**IFF (Identification Friend or Foe) transponder aerial**
**Laser Ranger and Marked Target Seeker**
**Pilot**
The pilot sits on a Martin-Baker Mk 9D rocket-powered ejection seat, which allows the pilot to escape if he loses control of if the aircraft is badly damaged. A safe ejection can be made from ground level upwards, even without forward speed. The rocket motor gives a smooth acceleration away from the stricken aircraft.
**Aden cannon**
Two 30-mm Aden cannons are mounted in pods slung under the fuselage. Each pod also contains 150 rounds of ammunition. They can be used against ground and air targets.
**Nozzle**
The Harrier's four engine nozzles can be rotated to point vertically downwards to allow the aircraft to take off or land vertically. They can also be vectored while the aircraft is in flight to enhance combat manoeuvrability.
**Fuel tank**
The Harrier almost always carries 455-litre fuel tanks on its inboard underwing pylons to extend its range. For short-range missions weapons can be carried on these pylons.

### *Laser Ranger and Marked Target Seeker*

The Ferranti LRMTS sends out pulses of laser energy and analyses the reflections to pinpoint the target so that weapons can be aimed exactly. Alternatively, the unit can search for and home onto reflected energy from a ground-based laser unit.

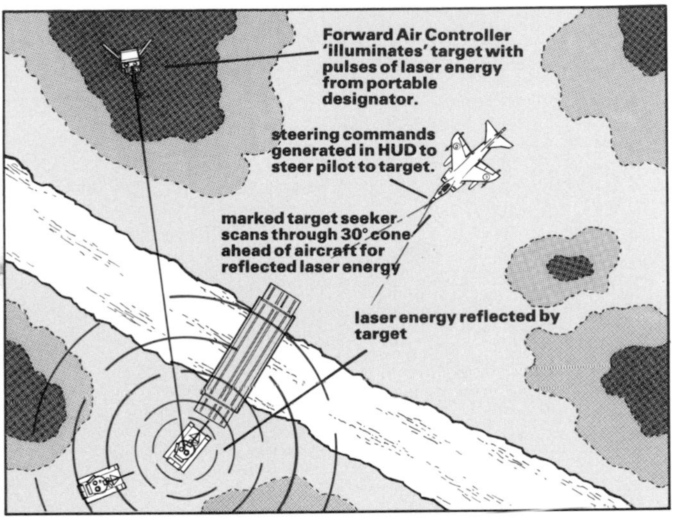
Forward Air Controller 'illuminates' target with pulses of laser energy from portable designator.
steering commands generated in HUD to steer pilot to target.
marked target seeker scans through 30° cone ahead of aircraft for reflected laser energy
laser energy reflected by target

aiming and release cues can be generated in the HUD.

In the high-threat environment of Western Europe the Harrier will rely on flying at high speed and ultra low-level (700 mph and 30 metres) to avoid enemy fire. A Marconi ARI 18223 RWR (Radar Warning Receiver) warns the pilot if hostile radar finds the aircraft.

## *Warning to pilot*

It classifies these radars by type, signal strength and direction, and presents a warning in the pilot's headset and visually on a small cathode ray tube. A Tracor ALE-40 chaff/flare dispenser is installed in the rear fuselage, and a Philips-MATRA Phimat chaff/flare dispenser pod can be carried on an underwing pylon. AIM-9L Sidewinder air-to-air missiles can be carried for self-defence.

The Harrier GR.Mk 3 carries a Ferranti Laser Ranger and Marked Target Seeker in the nose cone, behind metal 'eyelid' shutters. The laser emits pulses of laser light every two to 10 seconds, using their reflections to

***Below left: The Harrier can deploy almost anywhere at a moment's notice. This one is seen in its revetment at 'Belize International' airport.***

***Below: When No. 1 Squadron sends its aircraft to Norway they receive a temporary winter camouflage, and operate from small civil airfields.***

## 30-mm Aden cannon

The 30-mm Aden cannon has been the standard British aircraft gun since the advent of the Hawker Hunter. The Harrier carries two of these weapons in belly pods, each with up to 150 rounds of ammunition. The GR.Mk 5 uses the similar but brand new Royal Ordnance Factory-manufactured 25-mm Aden.

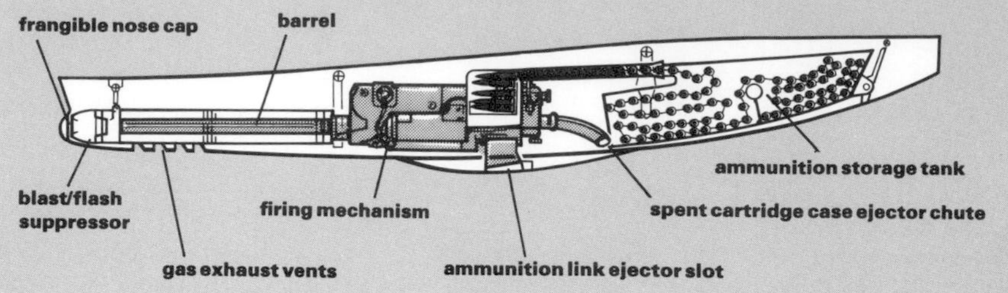


ascertain range, closure rate and other information. The marked target seeker is used to detect and home in on laser energy reflected by a target that has been illuminated by a ground-based laser designator.

### *Range of targets*

The Harrier can use its sophisticated systems to deliver a wide range of weaponry onto various types of target, including tanks, soft-skinned vehicles, troops and defensive positions. The Harrier makes a crucial contribution to the land battle simply by being available to intervene at a moment's notice, when other aircraft may be unable to take off from their

# Battlefield Evaluation: comparing

## British Aerospace Harrier GR.Mk 3

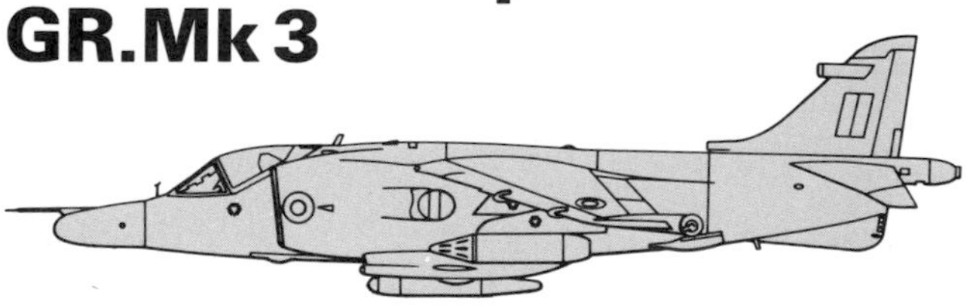

The Royal Air Force is the only user of the Harrier GR.Mk 3, with two squadrons in Germany, one in the UK and a handful of aircraft in Belize. The aircraft has, by modern standards, a primitive inertial-based nav/attack system, although the Ferranti Laser Ranger and Marked Target Seeker improves weapons-aiming accuracy. Radar warning receivers, ECM equipment and chaff/flare dispensers have been fitted.

**Specification:**
**Length overall:** 14.27 m
**Wing span:** 7.70 m
**Maximum speed at sea level:** 634 knots
**Combat radius lo-lo-lo:** 370 km (with 1360-kg external load)
**Maximum weapon load:** 3630 kg
**Take-off distance:** vertical, or up to 300 metres at maximum weight

**Assessment**
**Manoeuvrability** *****
**Rough-field capability** *****
**Versatility** *****
**Robustness** **

***The Harrier is one of the most important and versatile close support aircraft in the NATO inventory.***

## SEPECAT Jaguar GR.Mk 1A

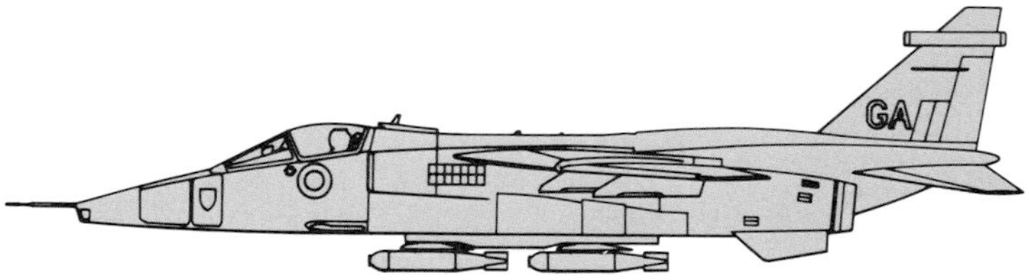


The Jaguar was designed from the outset for operation at high speed and ultra low-level. Its Rolls-Royce Turboméca Adour turbofans give low specific fuel consumption, allowing an impressive radius of action. Modern, highly-sophisticated avionics, including the Ferranti NAVWASS (Navigation and Weapons Aiming Sub-System), permit the aircraft to find and hit its target with unerring accuracy in all weathers.

**Specification:**
**Length overall:** 16.83 m
**Wing span:** 8.69 m
**Maximum speed at sea level:** 729 knots
**Combat radius lo-lo-lo:** 917 km
**Maximum weapon load:** 4763 kg
**Take-off distance:** 565 m

**Assessment**
**Manoeuvrability** **
**Rough-field capability** ****
**Versatility** ***
**Robustness** ***

***The Jaguar is a formidable close support aircraft, and serves with six air forces. This is an Indian aircraft.***

## General Dynamics F-16C Fighting Falcon

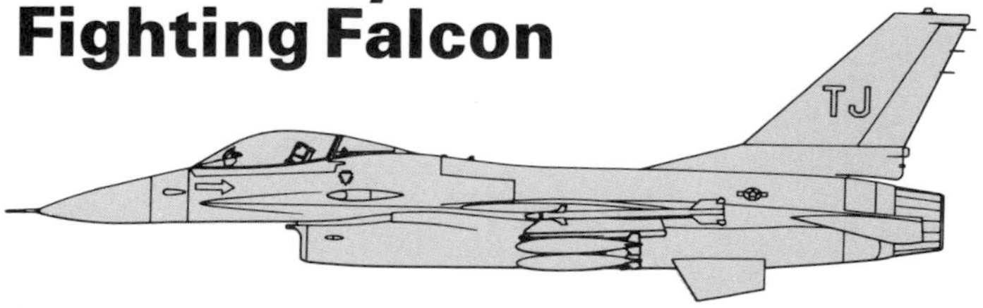


In any conflict NATO's F-16s will be heavily committed to air defence duties, but will retain a major ground attack commitment. The major weakness of the F-16 is its virtual inability to operate from semi-prepared forward airstrips. It can, however, carry a large weapon load over a respectable range, and deliver ordnance with great accuracy using its modern nav/attack systems.

**Specification:**
**Length overall:** 15.09 m
**Wing span:** 10.01 m
**Maximum speed at sea level:** 793 knots
**Combat radius lo-lo-lo:** 547 km
**Maximum weapon load:** 5443 kg
**Take-off distance:** 365 m

**Assessment**
**Manoeuvrability** *****
**Rough-field capability** **
**Versatility** ****
**Robustness** ***

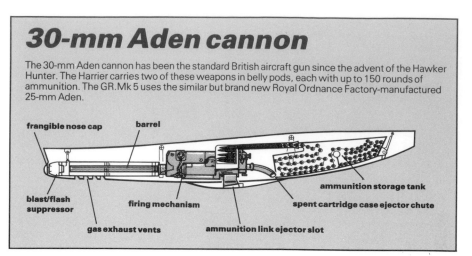

***The General Dynamics F-16 is probably the West's finest air-to-air fighter, but is also a useful ground-attack aircraft.***

damaged runways.

The GR.Mk 3 will soon be replaced by the GR.Mk5, with its updated avionics, improved aerodynamics and uprated engine. The GR.Mk 5 will offer much improved performance and accuracy, able to carry twice as big a warload over the same distance or the same warload over twice the distance.

With the GR.Mk 5 in service, the unofficial motto of the Gütersloh Harrier Wing will be even more welcome to hard pressed troops – "May the Force be with you!"

***This No. 3 Squadron Harrier is seen toting a pair of 1,000-lb Paveway laser-guided bombs underwing.***

# the Harrier with its rivals

## Mikoyan Gurevich MiG-27 'Flogger'

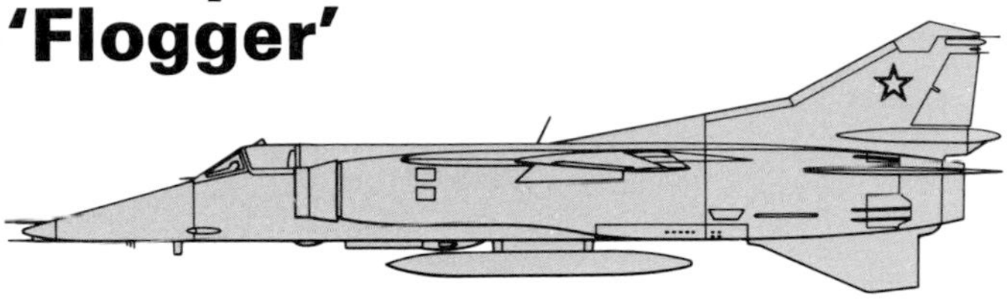

Vast numbers of 'Floggers' are in service with Warsaw Pact air arms and with Soviet Frontal Aviation. Most are intercept-optimised MiG-23s, with a formidable ground attack capability, although large numbers of dedicated attack MiG-23BMs and BNs and MiG-27s are also in service. These aircraft are fitted with comprehensive attack avionics and a new heavily-armoured cockpit with an improved field of view over the 'ducknose'.

**Specification:**
**Length overall:** 16.00 m
**Wing span:** 8.17 m; (spread) 14.25 m
**Maximum speed at sea level:** (estimated) 725 knots
**Combat radius lo-lo-lo:** (estimated) 390 km
**Maximum weapon load:** (estimated) 4000 kg
**Take-off distance:** (clean) 2200 m

**Assessment**

| | |
|---|---|
| **Manoeuvrability** | *** |
| **Rough-field capability** | *** |
| **Versatility** | ** |
| **Robustness** | ***** |

***The MiG-27 'Flogger-J' has advanced avionics, and is the most sophisticated member of the attack 'Flogger' family.***

## Sukhoi Su-17 'Fitter-K'

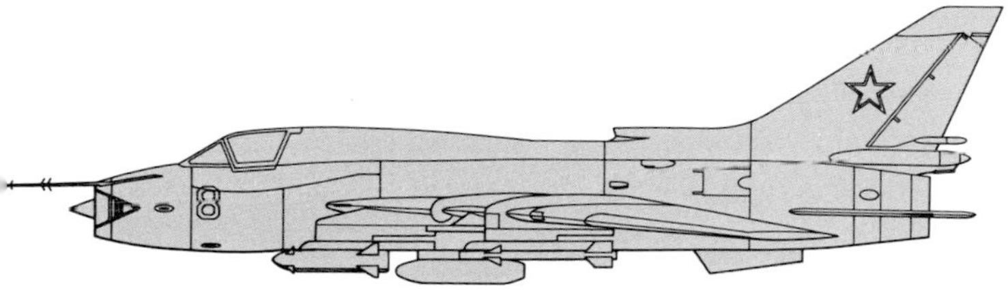

Backbone of the ground attack arms of many Warsaw Pact air forces, the 'swing-wing' Sukhoi 'Fitter' is built like a tank, and is intended for operation from semi-prepared forward airfields. Compared with the original Su-7 'Fitter', the Su-17's new variable-geometry wing and new engine give lower fuel consumption, longer range and greater payload. More modern avionics are also fitted.

**Specification:**
**Length overall:** 19.20 m
**Wing span:** 10.60 m; (spread) 14.00 m
**Maximum speed at sea level:** (estimated) 695 knots
**Combat radius lo-lo-lo:** (estimated) 360 km
**Maximum weapon load:** 3000 kg
**Take-off distance:** (clean) 610 m

**Assessment**

| | |
|---|---|
| **Manoeuvrability** | *** |
| **Rough-field capability** | *** |
| **Versatility** | *** |
| **Robustness** | **** |

***A Su-17 'Fitter-K' of the Polish air force is seen at low level. The Su-17/20 family is in widespread service.***

## Sukhoi Su-25 'Frogfoot'

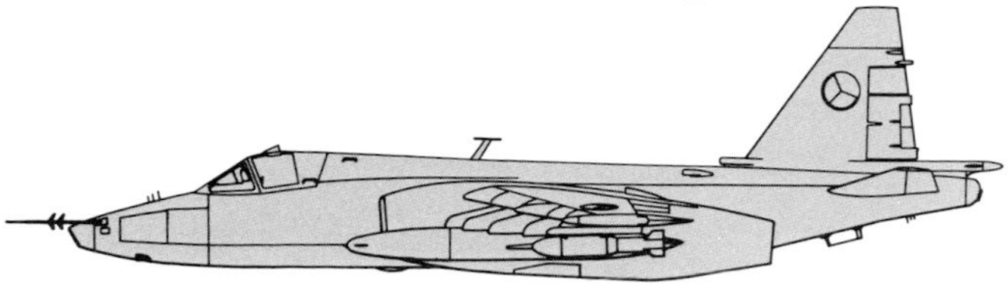

The 'Frogfoot' is the Warsaw Pact's equivalent to the A-10 Thunderbolt, but due to its powerful turbojet engines is rather faster, with a shorter take-off run. The aircraft is highly manoeuvrable and is fitted with chaff/flare dispensers and ECM jammers. The aircraft has seen active service in Afghanistan and in the Gulf War. Soviet Su-25s frequently co-operate with Mil Mi-24 'Hind' helicopters.

**Specification:**
**Length overall:** 14.50 m
**Wing span:** 15.50 m
**Maximum speed at sea level:** (estimated) 475 knots
**Combat radius lo-lo-lo:** (estimated) 544 km
**Maximum weapon load:** (estimated) 4000 kg
**Take-off distance:** (estimated) 472 m

**Assessment**

| | |
|---|---|
| **Manoeuvrability** | **** |
| **Rough-field capability** | **** |
| **Versatility** | * |
| **Robustness** | **** |

***The Su-25 'Frogfoot' is one of the most useful close support aircraft in service, being fast, agile and rugged.***

# Using Your Survival Knife

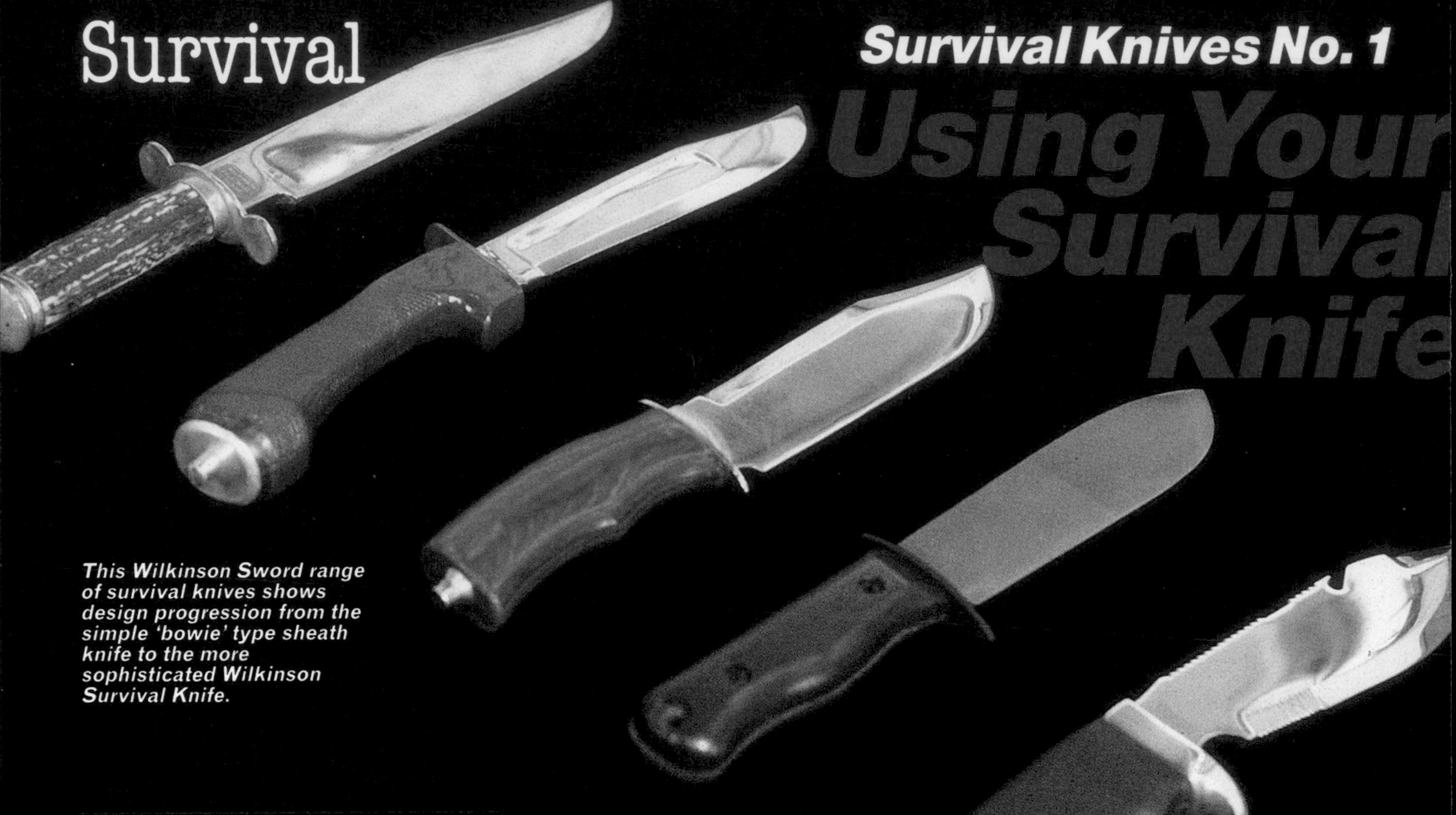

*This Wilkinson Sword range of survival knives shows design progression from the simple 'bowie' type sheath knife to the more sophisticated Wilkinson Survival Knife.*

***Your choice of survival knife speaks of your knowledge of survival; the state it is in and the way in which you use it speak of your experience.*** To a survivor, a knife is the most versatile life-saving aid. To a survival expert it is a craftsman's tool, treated with the same care and attention as a master carpenter's chisels. It is not toyed with; it remains in its sheath until it is needed, and is then used with great dexterity and ease for a multitude of tasks before being returned to its resting place.

## The grip

The grip is the best place to begin your personalisation. It is an essential feature of your knife, and must allow for exact and secure control of the blade in many differing uses and environments.

**1** If a grip is too large you will not be able to hold onto it for heavy cutting.

**2** If a grip is too small you will have to clench it tightly for heavy cutting; this is very tiring and dangerous. Blisters and severe hand cramps can result.

**3** If a grip is too long it may pull out from your hand.

**4** If a grip is too short you will not be able to hold onto the knife correctly, which may be dangerous.

As a general rule, it is better to have a grip that is slightly too big, as it is less tiring to use than a too-small grip – and when your hand tires you will have accidents. A large grip is easier to hold when wearing gloves. Your grip should be easy to hold in a variety of different ways, with no sharp edges or protuberances that will impede its use. It should be the correct shape in cross section, which is a blunt oval shape.

## Improving the shape

**1** If your grip is too round you may be able to build it up using Gaffa tape or nylon webbing and a strong resin. Very often round grips are all-metal: these are best covered, as metal is a 'non-friendly' material, hot in the desert, dangerously freezing in the Arctic and always hard. Remember that whatever you use as a grip covering must be resilient to a variety of temperatures and environmental conditions.

**2** If your grip is too square you may (if the grip material is soft or man-made) be able to file or sand it to the correct shape. This is preferable to covering because the performance of the grip will not be impaired by changing climates.

**3** If your grip is of bone it may feel as though it is more comfortable when gripped as for hammering. In this case there is usually little that can be done other than replacing the grip entirely.

## Grip cross-sections

Altering the grip may seem a drastic thing to do, but once the knife fits your hand, there will be a vast improvement in its effectiveness as it will take less effort to use.

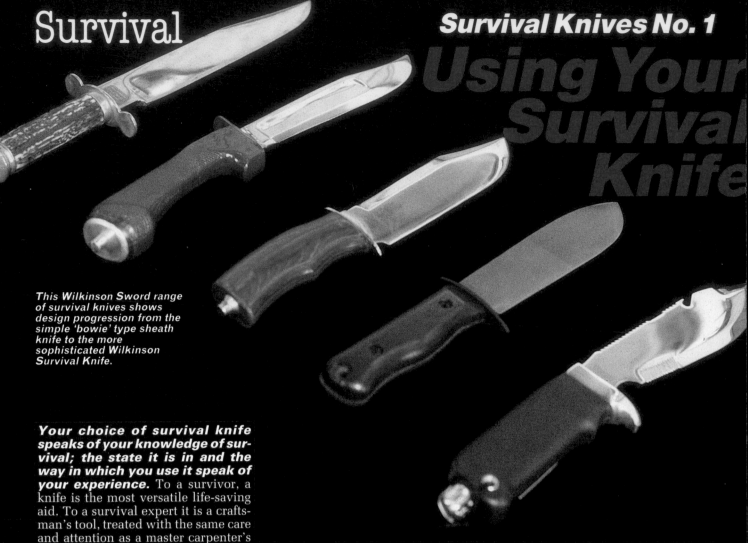

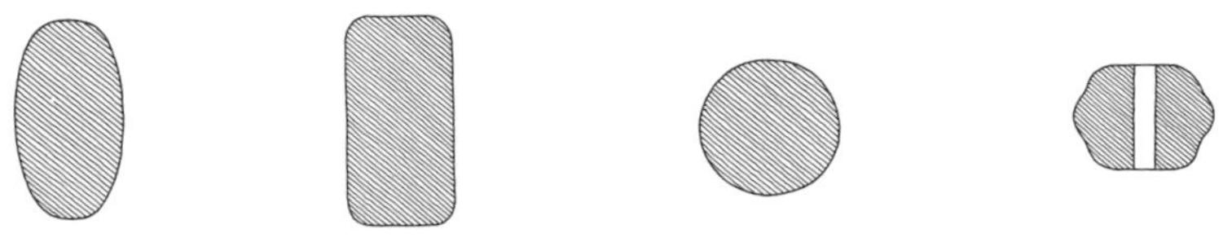

**The best shape for the grip.**

**Too square: this will need reducing.**

**Too round: this will need to be built up.**

**Antler handles are not suitable: substitute a better-shaped grip.**

# Common uses for your knife

**Slashing**
Grip the knife as far back as possible. Use long, sweeping motions with a straight arm.

**Chopping**
Grip the knife further forward, with your cutting action more from the elbow than the shoulder.

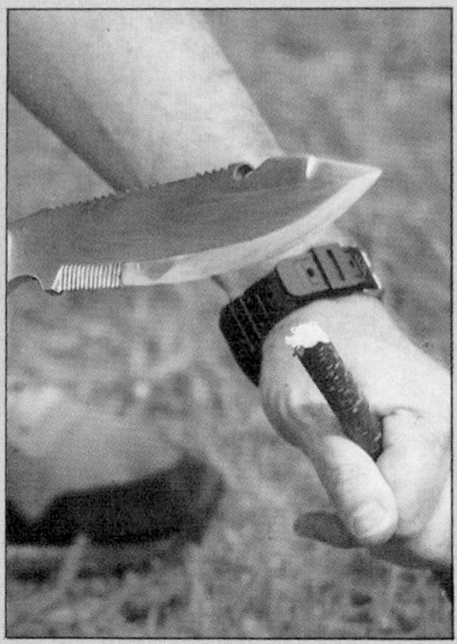

**Hammering**
Use the flat of the blade, keeping the edge aimed away from your body.

**Stake pointing**
Hold the grip even further forward and, using mainly wrist action, cut away from you.

**Draw knife**
Fit a makeshift split stick-handle to the point end of your knife.

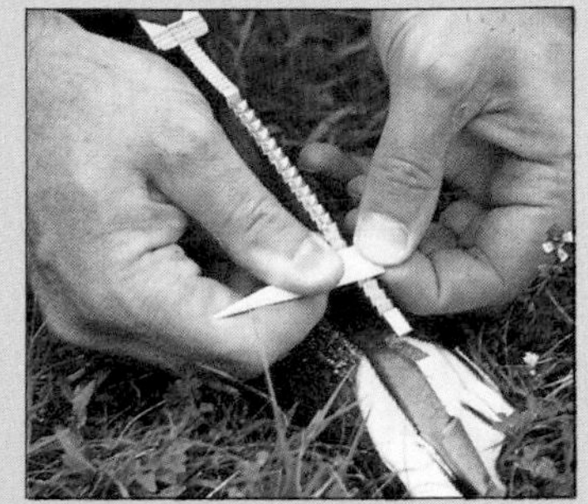

**Rasping**
If your knife has a saw back, you can set it into a log and work bone on it.

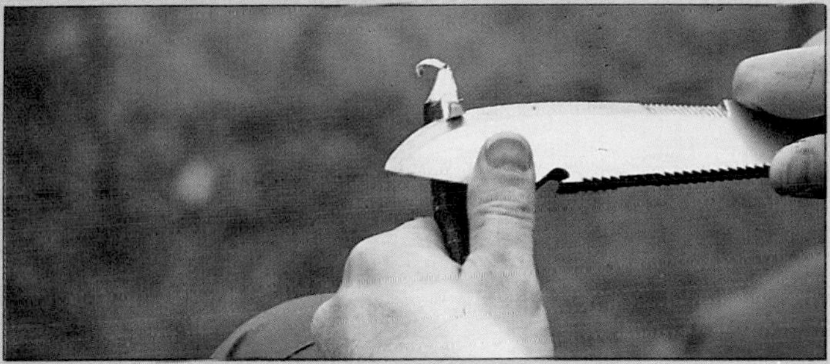

**Whittling**
Control is the name of the game. If you can lever with the thumb of your free hand, on the back of the blade, do so. Otherwise take your time with many small, shallow cuts.

**Sawing**
Sawing is not designed to cut through wood but is mainly for grooving wood and cutting ropes. Cut on the draw stroke.

**Splitting**
This is an important operation. Strike the blade through the work piece with a wooden baton (not stone or metal).

# Parallel honing

Once you have a professional edge, make sure you do not destroy it while honing. A common failing is to tilt the edge too sharply; this gradually blunts the knife. These cross-sections of the blade show the right and wrong methods, and the results of each.

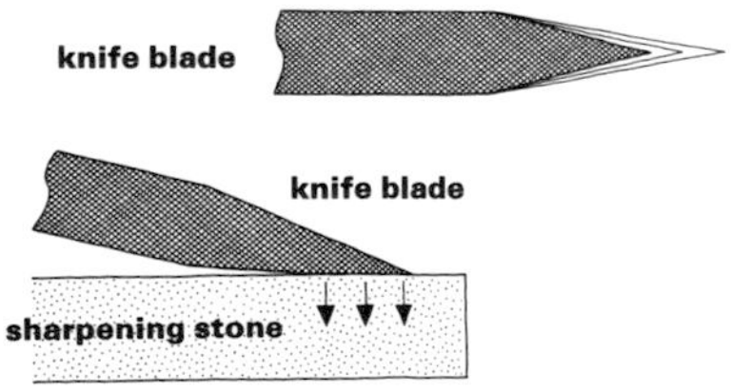


**WRONG:** Pressure is greatest near the edge.

Sharpening with too much pressure on the edge of the blade progressively changes the cutting angle, blunting the knife. The only remedy is to have the whole edge re-ground: an expensive business. In the field, the knife will become blunter and more difficult to sharpen.

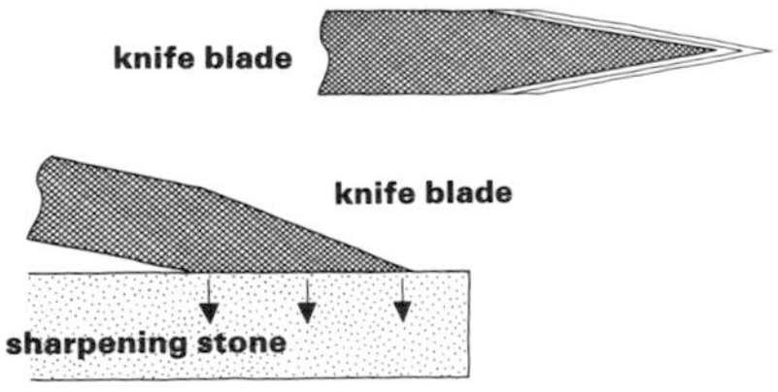


**RIGHT:** Pressure is exerted at a shallower angle.

Maintaining the pressure in the correct way retains the cutting edge. Patience is the essential ingredient: remember that a blunt knife is not just an inefficient tool, but is also dangerous.

### *The blade*

Having set up the grip, give your knife a 'road test': there should be an immediate and definite improvement in its performance. But the blade is where the major transformation will occur. You will have to alter the angle of the edge, to improve its cutting ability, which in most cases means a long session of filing. Avoid using a high-speed grinding wheel, unless you are very expert in its use, and back-street knife sharpeners, as the risk of the blade overheating and losing its temper is high.

To help you, some of the better established knife manufacturers will supply a knife with a 'professional edge', but only on request. Once the edge has been altered you should

## Rockwell testing

When the knife is ready to be finished it is carefully tested to check that is has been correctly tempered. The steel of the blade is indented with a diamond tool at a set pressure. The softer the steel, the deeper and wider the dent made by the tool. A reading of this indentation is taken: in the case of the steel used for the Wilkinson Sword Survival Knife, a reading of 54-55 Rockwell C is correct. 52 would be too soft, reducing the edge retention, and 57 would be too hard, causing brittleness.

The master grinder shapes the edge on a rotating whetstone. The stone is 1½ metres in diameter, so the grinder sits astride it on a saddle-like seat.

The master polisher puts a mirror finish on the blade: a slow and patient task. He uses a series of buffers, from coarse to super-fine.

A master craftsman applies the 'professional edge': this is supplied only on request.

***Above: The display on the Rockwell testing machine clearly shows the diamond dent punched in the blade.***

***Right: The master grinder puts an edge on the knife.***

never have to re-grind the edge, because you will now 'parallel sharpen.'

### Sharpening

To sharpen your knife you will need a stone. The best type of stone is still a natural stone such as a Washita or Soft Arkansas stone, although there is much to be said for the strength of a diamond whetstone for field use.

At home base you should have a large stone. This makes sharpening an easy task, using six long strokes on the left of the blade, six on the right, and six alternately.

In the field you will need a small pocket stone, or failing this a suitable local stone or large pebble. Hold the knife steady and move the stone: the opposite to home sharpening.

Whenever you sharpen your blade, maintain an even pressure across the full width of the edge. If you place too much pressure on the edge itself you will not be sharpening parallel to the edge angle you originally laboured to achieve, but will be gradually blunting the knife.

### Honing

Having sharpened your knife, a really razor-like edge can be achieved by lightly honing with a ceramic rod. Use this before all major cutting to help maintain the edge.

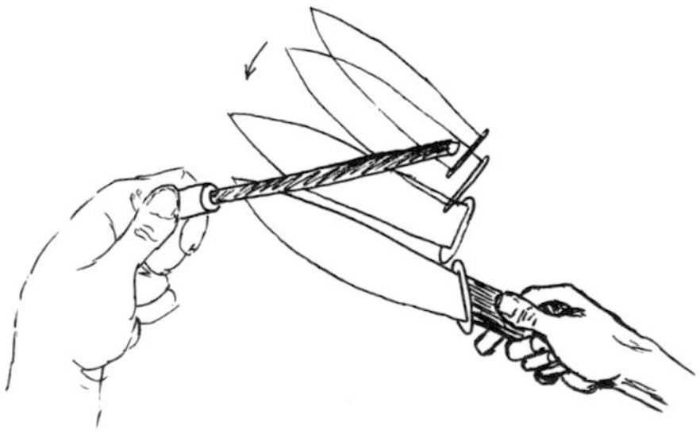

**Above:** Honing a razor edge with a steel or ceramic rod, use ten light strokes alternatively on each side of the edge. As each stroke nears the point the angle of the blade should become less acute.

**Left:** Polishing as part of producing a professional edge, definitely a worthwhile investment if you are serious about your knife.

### Profession use

In the hands of a professional a survival knife takes on jobs that seem impossible. This is because he has learned to use the correct cutting techniques and angles. Experience and practice will be your best guide here, although the most basic principles are:

**1** Safety first.
**2** Cut with the grain in your favour.
**3** Always follow through.
**4** Use smooth, steady cuts, the fewer the better.

### Making other tools

A professional's knife is a tool to make other tools. Wherever possible he avoids any use of the knife which may result in its damage or loss. If a root needs to be dug up, make a digging stick; if a spear point is needed, whittle one.

### Safety first

**1** When you carry your knife, carry a first aid kit.
**2** Plan every cut before you make it.
**3** Keep all limbs away from the arc of your cut.
**4** *Always* cut away from the body.
**5** Be aware of what is going on around you.
**6** Replace the knife in its scabbard immediately after use.
**7** Never lend your knife; you may never see it again.

### IMPORTANT

***The privilege of owning a survival knife is one that all survival students must uphold and defend. Be professional in your approach and use of your knife, and be seen to be professional.***

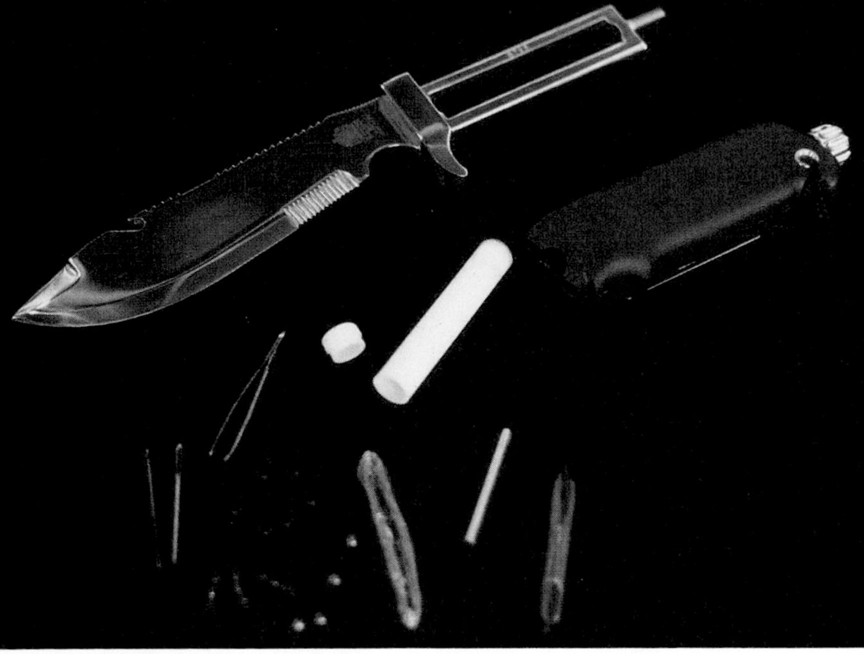

***The Wilkinson Sword Survival Knife and contents. It is designed to cope with a very wide range of tasks, from very fine skinning to heavy chopping and hammering. The aim is a single comprehensive survival tool from which you are never separated. The deer below was grallocked (gutted), skinned and butchered using only this knife.***

# Preparing a deer

Gutting, skinning and halving usually requires two knives and a saw. If you can achieve this with one knife, you've got a good survival knife.

**1 Cut off the head** as close to the base of the skull as possible by cutting through to the bone and chopping through it.

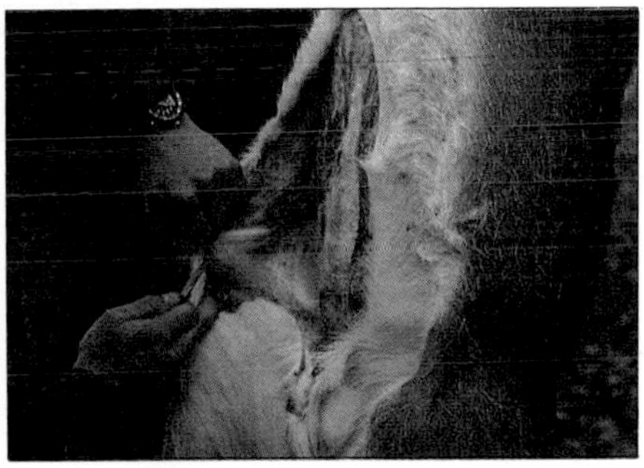

**2 Start at the base of the sternum** and pull the skin away as you cut. Leave as little flesh or fat on the skin as possible.

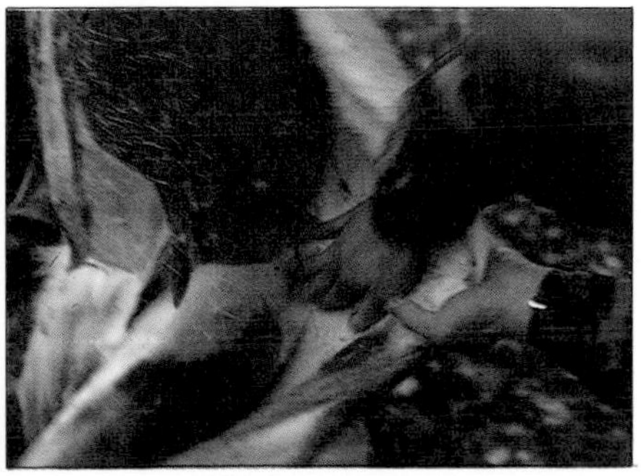

**3 The skin comes off quite easily** and you should be able to use your hands for most of it.

**4 Cut round the windpipe,** separating it from the flesh of the neck.

**5 Start at the sternum** and cut carefully down to the pelvis. Push your hands up on each side, cut round the diaphragm and grasp the windpipe or the heart and lungs and pull down.

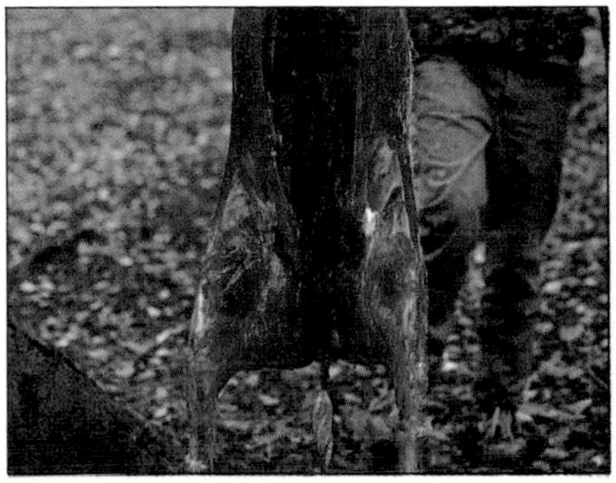

**6 Heart and lungs** and all the guts should come out in one piece. You will need to cleaver through the pelvic basin.

**7 Halving** Your knife must be heavy enough for cleavering through bone to butcher, extract marrow and split the skull.

# Choosing Your Survival Knife

*The Al-Mar Sere 6 is a beautifully crafted knife, but a little too light for heavy chopping and cleaving.*

A civilian stranded after a disaster such as a shipwreck or a plane crash will not have chosen a survival knife. He will have to make do with whatever he's got with him – perhaps a piece of sharpened fuselage, or at best a Swiss Army Knife. But soldiers and adventurers operating in remote regions of the world will almost certainly have a knife with them at all times, and they will have made a choice.

The wrong choice could be fatal, as a knife is literally a lifeline in the wilderness, upon which you must be able to rely completely. It's too late to find out your knife is not strong enough when you are trying to cut yourself free from a capsized white water raft heading for a waterfall!

## Survival knife?

When choosing your knife, find a reputable dealer with a large range of quality knives. Often the best shops stock custom knifemaker ranges.

Do not limit your choice of knife to those described as 'Survival Knives'; there are many hunting knives eminently suited to survival use. Try also to be practical. There are many beautiful knives for sale, well made and by top-class manufacturers; but they are not all practical for the specialised use you will be demanding.

You must always carry your knife with you; you never know when you'll need it. This means that your knife must be a convenient size to be carried without becoming a drag, and must also be capable of carrying out all those basic camp chores such as opening tins, hammering tent pegs, cutting string and so on. And if you become stranded or have to go to ground it will have to do the job of a small axe as well, so it must be strong. Generally speaking, a fixed blade is the better option as it is stronger and more rugged, but most professionals carry two knives: a large fixed blade and a small folding blade.

## What metal?

There are really only two basic choices: carbon steel or stainless steel.

*Traditionally, soldiers have purchased their own knives to take into battle. Note the Gerber Mark 2, excellent as a fighting knife but of limited use in survival.*

Carbon steel will rust (generally speaking) unless cared for, whereas stainless steel should not. It is widely recognised that carbon steel takes a keener edge than stainless, although in some modern aircraft and cutlery, stainless steels are challenging this traditional concept. Stainless steel should hold its edge longer than carbon steel, but is in many cases harder to sharpen.

In most cases, stainless steel would be the best choice. Take the advice of a reputable dealer, as there are many varieties in use, in many cases alloyed with other metals such as vanadium, molybdenum and chromium to change their qualities. In general, avoid divers' knives (unless made by a reputable manufacturer), as the steel is usually very poor.

When you are finding out about the type of steel used, try also to find out about the temper. If a knife is under-tempered it will be strong but will not take an edge; if it is over-tempered, it could shatter in use. There is a tendency for manufacturers to over-temper blades!

## Size, weight and balance

The wise traveller tries to reduce the weight of his pack, but when travelling far off the beaten track don't try to economise on the weight of your knife. You need a knife with a weighty blade, as this reduces the force you need to apply and allows more control and efficiency. But if you choose a blade that is too heavy, it will cause fatigue in your fingers, wrist and arm, and this can lead to dangerous accidents.

The length and weight of your knife are critical factors, but no real formula exists to help you choose. In jungles, machetes and long, light knives are the norm, but for more general use these are really too long. As a rough guide, don't choose a knife that is more than two and a half times the length of your hand, and no less than one and a half times long.

## Leverage principle

To illustrate the principle, imagine that you are striking a nail into a piece of wood with a one-metre steel bar. If you want to achieve the same result with a bar 50 centimetres long, you must either use a lot more force or a heavier bar. The shorter, heavier bar is more controllable as it exerts less leverage on the wrist, and can be used in more confined space. The same is true of knife lengths.

Once you have chosen the length and weight of your blade, try to decide where the point of balance lies. Ideally it should be just in front of the guard. This means that the knife is slightly blade-heavy, yet easily controlled by adjusting your grip.

If the point of balance is too far forward it will cause muscle strain, which makes the knife slip from your grasp. The more common fault is that the knife is too handle-heavy. Excess weight in the grip is a burden, as it does not contribute to the blade's cutting ability.

# The parts of a survival knife

In war, there is no room for the amateur. You must have the right knife for the job and be skilled in its use: you won't have time to start thinking about it if you're on the brink of a war zone.

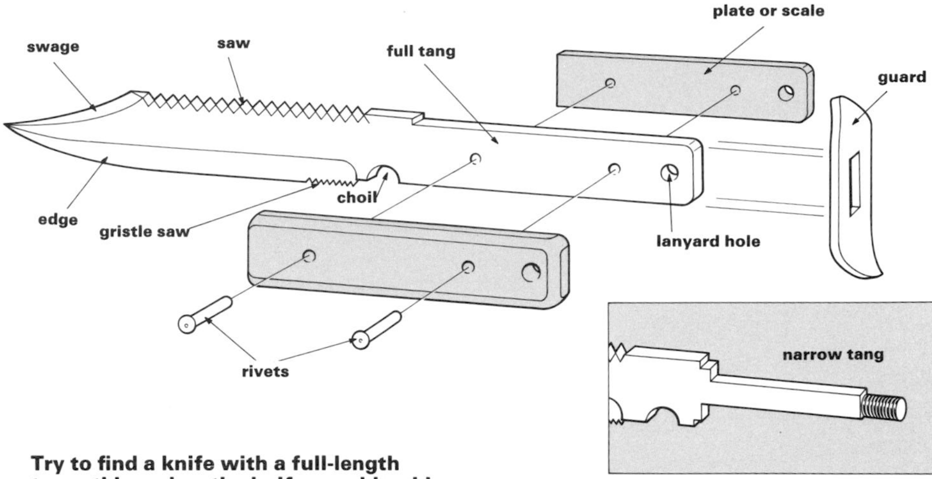


**Try to find a knife with a full-length tang; this makes the knife considerably stronger.**

## Features and fittings

The most important fitting to your knife is the grip; probably the commonest fault in most survival knives is the way by which the grip is attached. The part of the blade that goes to make up the handle is called the 'tang'.

***This American pilot in Vietnam is sporting a .357 Magnum revolver and US issue aircrew survival knife, while the SEAL carries a Gerber fighting knife.***

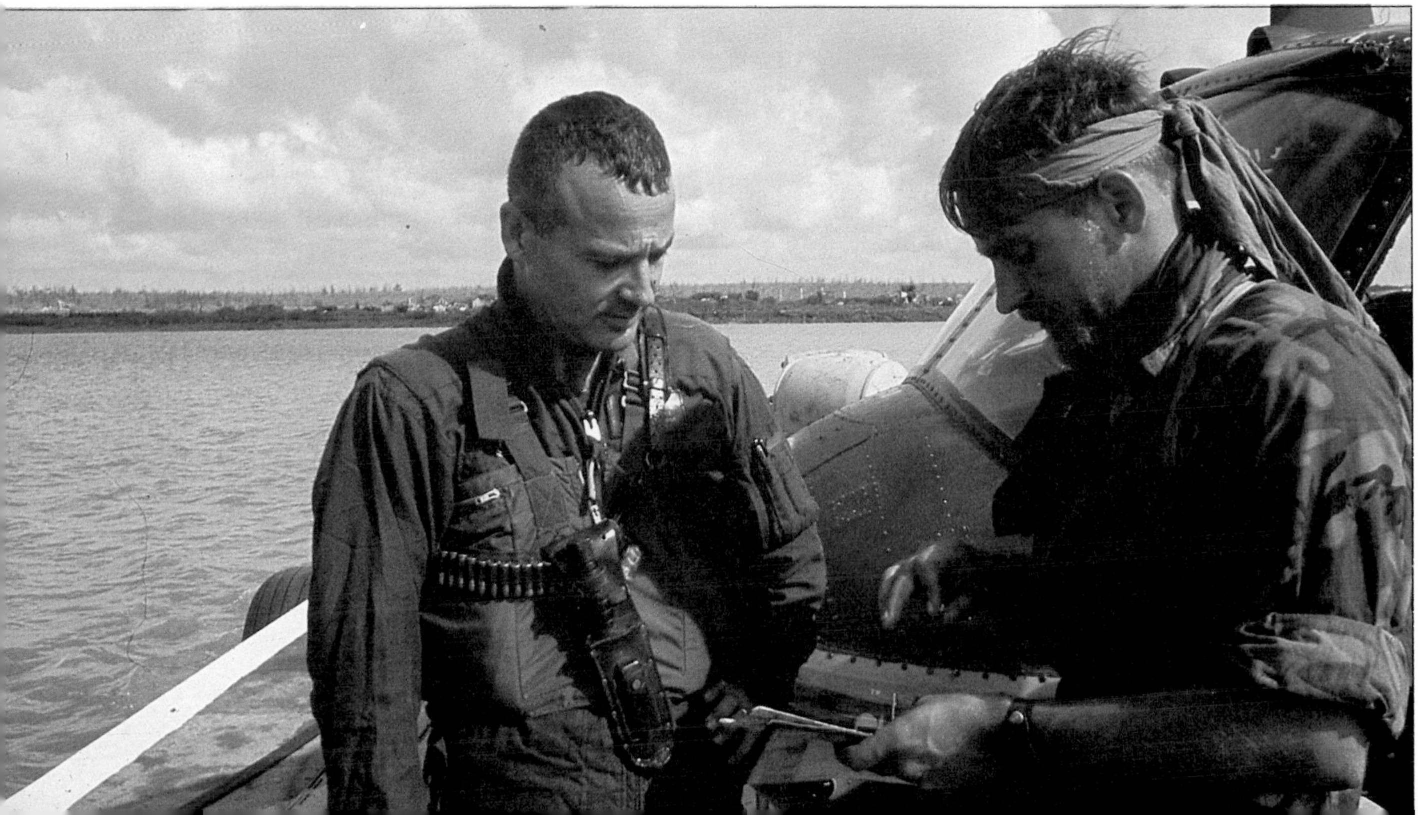

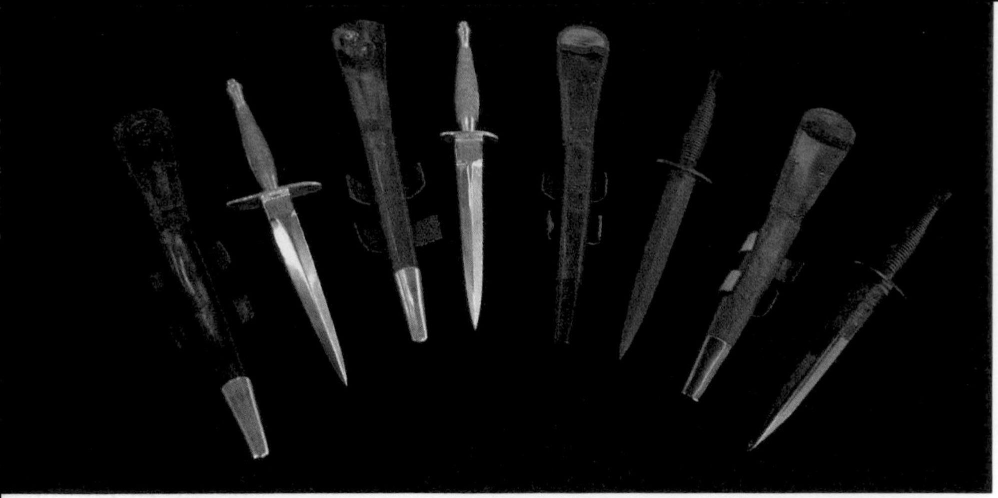

This is **Wilkinson Sword's** range of Commando daggers, from the original Sykes-Fairburn to the later production model. These are fighting knives and have very little survival application. Double-edged weapons cannot be used for skinning or fine cutting as the finger cannot be placed on the back of the blade for control, and they are too light for chopping or cleaving. You are better off with a survival knife that has a variety of functions.

**The Cold Steel Tanto**
A very strong knife with a very comfortable grip and designed to incorporate Western and Oriental ideas, this is a good fighting knife but again has limited chopping capability.

**The Robert Parrish knife**
A 20-cm survival and combat knife, this is a good all-rounder although it does not have a full tang. It has a hollow handle for survival kit.

**The Jimmy Lile Sly 2** (top) and the **Rambo** (below)
As seen in the movies: good quality, but a little too large for fine cutting. Both have hollow handles and a thong eye in the butt.

**The Survival Aids Explora survival knife**
This features a survival kit, sharping stone, wirecutters, compass, a screwdriver tip and removable handguard and, of course, saw-back blade.

**The Tekna Wilderness Edge**
This features a survival kit stored in the sheath, a Tekna torch in the handle, a honing stone and flint, and a 15-cm blade.

**The Eikhorn survival knife**
This well-made German knife with a bowie type blade with thumb rest and hollow handle, again suffers from not really being heavy enough.

In many knives, this narrows at the join of the guard and grip. This is an inherent weakness, at the point of greatest strain. The ideal attachment is what is called 'full tang', where the blade remains the width of the grip throughout.

Hollow handles often mean that the tang not only narrows but shortens as well. While not all hollow handles are weak, take great care in your choice.

The guard is an important feature of any survival knife. Its purpose is to prevent your fingers slipping forward onto the sharp edge while using the knife. Remember: even the smallest cut can fester and prove fatal under survival conditions.

The point of your knife is another important feature. It needs to be sharp, and strong enough to pry with. It is an advantage if it falls below the horizontal mid-line of your knife: this is a 'true drop point', and prevents the point snagging the flesh of an animal's stomach wall during skinning and gutting.

## Saws and hollow handles

Saws are a regular feature of survival knives. Do not expect them to saw through wood. They will, however, cut grooves in wood and cut ropes, making them a useful additional feature although not essential.

Gristle saws are sometimes found in front of the guard. These again are a useful additional feature that will find many uses.

Hollow handles are designed to accommodate useful survival tools such as fishing lines or firelighting

***An East German border guard photographs the West German border guards, equipped with an AKM and an interesting stiletto dagger that looks remarkably like a Sykes-Fairburn.***

**Machetes**
Great for jungle work, but of limited use for anything else. The kukri (right) is a good cleavering and cutting knife, but is no good for fine cutting or hammering.

**Army issue: Golok and SLR bayonet**
The Golok is a popular survival knife, and can be improved by regrinding the edge and shortening the grip. The SLR bayonet is useless as a survival knife.

***A US Army Ranger poses complete with hatchet. Try to select a knife that will do the job of a knife and hatchet; your personal kit will be heavy enough without duplication.***

**The Buckmaster**
Seen as *the* survival knife for some time, it has a hollow handle and detachable anchor pins. It can be used in conjunction with rope as a grappling hook for climbing walls etc!

**The Buck Hunter and Ranger**
These are excellent-quality lock blades for fine cutting. This is the only additional type of knife you should consider carrying in addition to your survival knife.

aids, and as long as they do not weaken the grip are an excellent addition.

### Sheaths

Sheaths are an important feature of any knife. As well as protecting the knife, they must be strong enough to protect you from injury if you fall on the encased blade. Good-quality leather sheaths are almost as good as the very strong scabbards being made from modern plastics, but beware of cheap leather. If you find a good knife that has a poor sheath you may be able to have a better sheath made for it.

**The Buck Kalinga and Akonua**
These are top quality presentation knives, ideal for skinning and cutting but too light for cleaving.

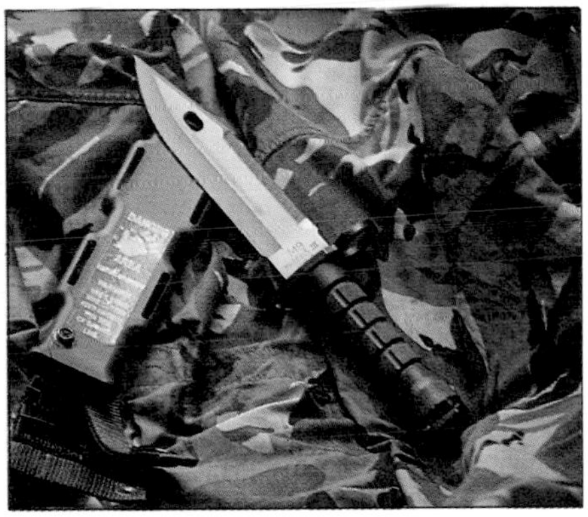

**The Buck M9 bayonet**
On issue to the US Army for use with the M16 A2, this is well thought out and well produced, falling somewhere between a knife and a bayonet.

The method of carrying the sheath is entirely up to you, and you may want to make some modifications. You may also consider taping additional survival gear to the outside of your scabbard, as long as you don't end up looking like a Christmas tree.

Having carefully selected your knife, work it in, personalise it, practise using it and, above all, look after it. Your life may one day depend on it.

# Crossing a River

***If you are on the run or are operating in wild terrain, you are likely to encounter water obstacles that you may have to cross. They may be fast-moving rivers or large, marshy areas of clinging, stinking and tiring mud.*** Each has its dangers, but also its drills for survival. Here we deal with rivers, using techniques from US Army Manual FM21-76.

### Finding your crossing-point

A river or stream may be narrow or wide, shallow or deep, slow-moving or fast-moving. It may be rain-fed, snow-fed or ice-fed. Your first step is to find a place where the river is basically safe for crossing, so look for a high place from which you can get a good view and look out for the best crossing point. If there is no high place, climb a tree.

***Crossing a water obstacle can be highly dangerous, especially to the untrained. If you are not equipped with inflatable rafts or other crossing equipment, you may need to build your own if you have to get kit or wounded men over the river.***

## Your first step

**Check the river carefully for the following features:**

**1** A level stretch where it breaks into a number of channels. Two or three narrow channels are usually easier to cross than a wide river.
**2** Obstacles on the opposite side of the river that might hinder your travel. Try to select the spot from which travel will be the safest and easiest.
**3** A ledge of rocks that crosses the river. This often indicates dangerous rapids or canyons.
**4** A deep or rapid waterfall or a deep channel. Never attempt to ford a stream directly above or even close to such spots.
**5** Rocky places. Avoid these; you can be seriously injured if you fall on rocks. An occasional rock that breaks the current, however, may assist you.
**6** A shallow bank or sandbar. If possible, select a point upstream from such a feature so that the current will carry you to it if you lose your footing.
**7** A course across the river that leads downstream, so that you can cross the current at about a 45° angle.

The depth of a fordable river or stream is no deterrent if you can keep your footing; in fact, deep water sometimes runs more slowly and is therefore safer than fast-moving shallow water. You can always dry your clothes later, or you can make a raft to carry your clothing and equipment across the river.

***British paratroops are seen using a raft to carry their equipment across a river during jungle warfare exercises. Deep, slow-moving water is easier to cross than shallower but faster-moving water.***

# Rafting a river

**Rafting rivers is one of the oldest forms of travel, and is often the safest and quickest method of crossing a water obstacle; however, building a raft under survival conditions is tiring and time-consuming unless you have proper equipment and help.**

## Brush and Australian ponch rafts

If you are with a companion and each of you has a poncho, you can construct a brush or Australian poncho raft. With this type of raft you can safely float your equipment across a slow-moving stream or river.

### Brush raft

The brush raft will support about 115 kg if properly constructed. Use ponchos; fresh, green brush; two small saplings; and a rope or vines.

**1** Tightly tie off the neck of each poncho with the neck drawstring.
**2** Attach ropes or vines at the corner and side grommets of each poncho. Be sure they are long enough to cross to and tie with those at the opposite corner or side.
**3** Spread one poncho on the ground with the tied-off hood upwards.
**4** Pile fresh, green brush (no thick branches) on the poncho until the brush stack is about 45 cm high.
**5** Pull the poncho neck drawstring up through the centre of the brush stack.
**6** Make an X-frame of two small saplings and place it on top of the brush stack.
**7** Tie the X-frame securely in place with the poncho neck drawstring.

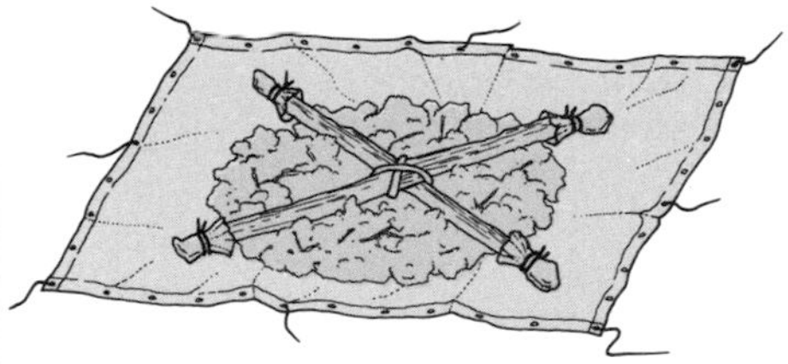

**8** Pile another 45 cm of brush on top of the X-frame.
**9** Compress the brush slightly.
**10** Pull the poncho sides up around the brush and, using the ropes or vines attached to the corner and side grommets, tie diagonally from corner to corner and from side to side.

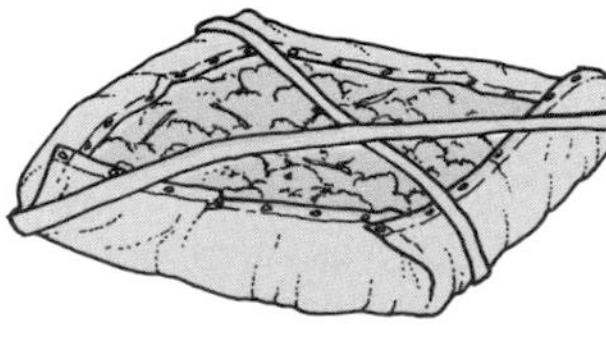

**11** Spread the second poncho, tied-off hood upwards, next to the brush bundle.

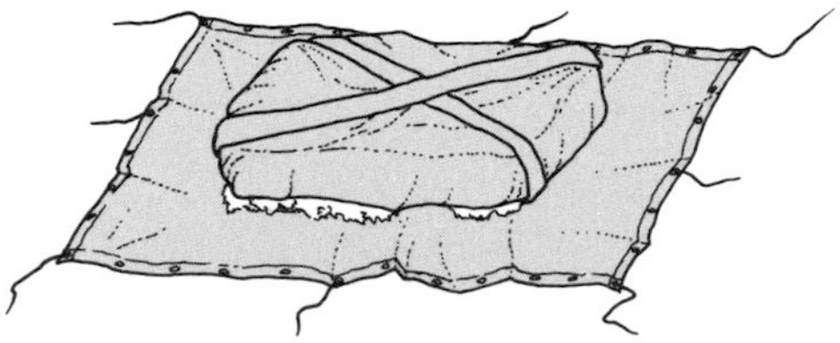

**12** Roll the brush bundle onto the centre of the second poncho so that the tied side faces downwards.
**13** Tie the second poncho around the brush bundle in the same way as you tied the first poncho around the brush (10).

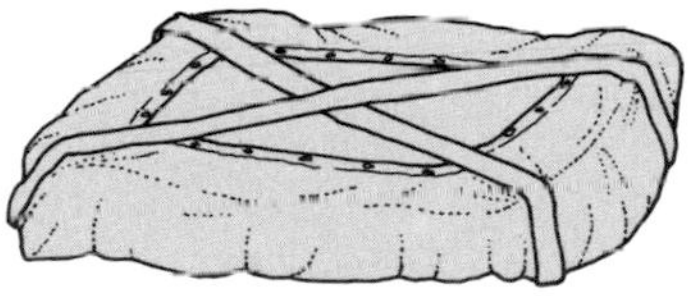

**14** Tie one end of a ripe to an empty canteen and the other end to the raft. This will help you to tow it.

### Australian poncho raft

If you do not have time to gather brush for a brush raft, you can make an Australian poncho raft. Although more waterproof, this will only float about 25 kg of equipment. Use two ponchos, two 1-metre poles or branches, and ropes, vines, bootlaces or comparable material.

**1** Tightly tie off the neck of each poncho with the neck drawstring.
**2** Spread one poncho on the ground with the neck upwards.
**3** Place and centre the two poles about 45 cm apart on the poncho.
**4** Place the rucksacks, packs and other equipment between the poles, including items that you want to keep dry, such as boots and outer garments.

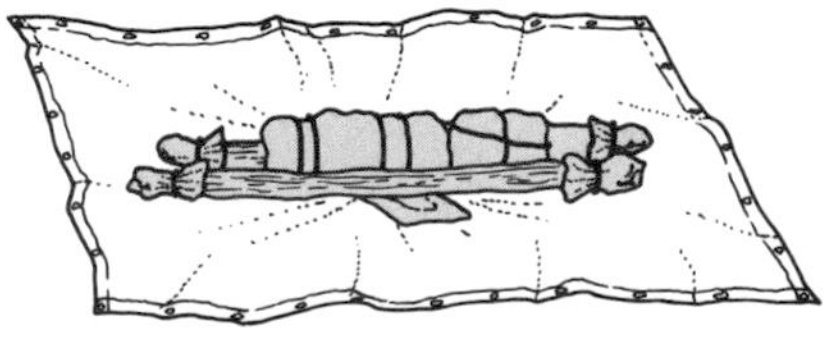

At this point you will need your companion's help to complete the raft.

**1** Snap the poncho sides together.
**2** Hold the snapped portion of the poncho in the air and roll it tightly down to the equipment. Make sure that you roll the full width of the poncho.
**3** Twist each end of the roll to form pigtails in opposite directions.
**4** Fold the pigtails over the bundle and tie them securely in place using ropes, vines or bootlaces.

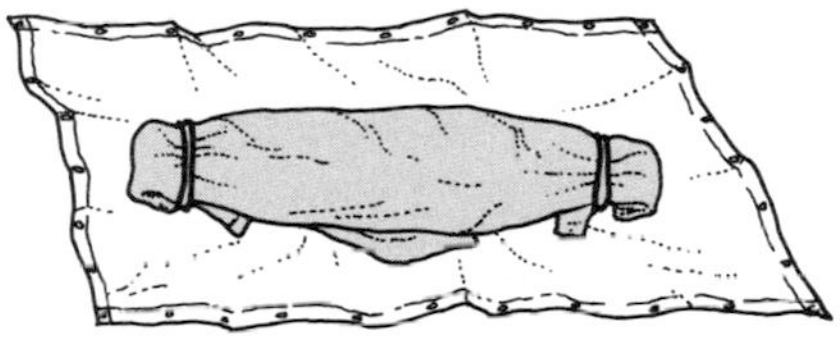

**5** Spread the second poncho on the ground with the tied-off hood upwards. If you need more buoyancy, place some fresh, green brush on this poncho.
**6** Place the equipment bundle, pigtail side down, on the centre of the second poncho.
**7** Wrap the second poncho around the equipment bundle following the same procedure as you used for wrapping the equipment in the first poncho.
**8** Tie ropes, vines or other binding material around the raft about 30 cm from each end of the pigtail.

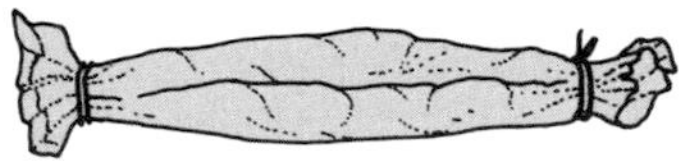

**9** Place and secure weapons on top of the raft.
**10** Tie one end of a ripe to a canteen and the other end to the raft. This will help you in towing the raft.

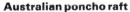

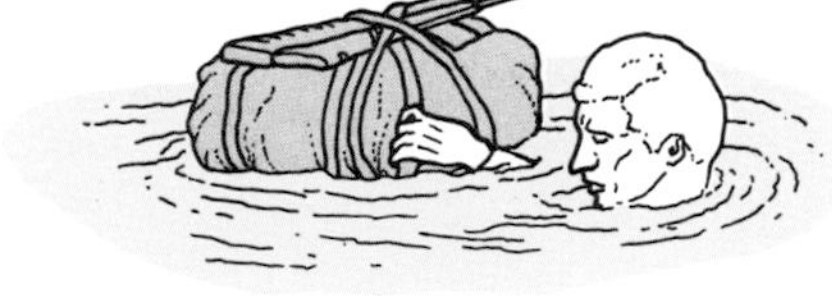

When launching or landing either type of raft, take care not to puncture or tear it by dragging it on the ground. Let the raft lie on the water for a few minutes to ensure that it floats before you start to cross the river or stream. If the river is too deep to ford, push the raft in front of you while swimming.

# Crossing a fast river

If you are going to ford a swift, treacherous stream, remove your trousers and underpants so that the water will have less grip on your legs. Keep your shoes on to protect your feet and ankles from rocks and to give you firmer footing. Tie your trousers and important articles securely to the top of your pack; if you have to release it, everything will be easier to find.

Carry your pack well up on your shoulders so that you can release it quickly if you are swept off your feet. Being unable to get a pack off quickly enough can drag even the strongest of swimmers under. Don't worry about the weight of your pack, as this will help rather than hinder you in fording the stream.

Find a strong pole about 12 cm in diameter and 2 to 2½ metres long to help you ford the stream. Grasp the pole and plant it firmly on your upstream side to break the current. Plant your feet firmly with each step, and move the pole forwards, slightly downstream from its previous position, but still upstream from you. With your next step, place your foot below the pole. Keep the pole well slanted so that the force of the current keeps the pole firmly against you.

**Cross the stream at a 45° angle, with the heaviest person on the downstream end of the pole.**

## Crossing as a team

If there are other people with you, cross the stream together. Make sure that everyone has prepared their pack and clothing as above. The heaviest person should be on the downstream end of the pole and the lightest person on the upstream end. This way, the upstream person will break the current, and the people below can move with comparative ease in the eddy formed by him. If the upstream person is temporarily swept off his feet, the others can hold him steady while he regains his footing.

As in all fording, cross the stream so that you will cross the downstream current at a 45° angle. Currents too strong for one person to stand

**This is a bird's-eye view of a four-man team**

### *Rapids*

Crossing a deep, swift river or rapids is not as dangerous as it looks. If you are swimming across, swim with the current – never fight it – and try to keep your body horizontal to the water. This will reduce the danger of being pulled under.

In fast, shallow rapids, travel on your back, feet first; use your hands as fins alongside your hips to add buoyancy and to fend off submerged rocks. Keep your feet up to avoid getting them bruised or caught by rocks.

In deep rapids, travel on your front, head first; angle towards the shore whenever you can. Breathe between wave troughs. Be careful of backwater eddies and converging currents as they often contain dangerous swirls.

***If you are crossing near the mouth of a silt-choked river avoid flat shores, which may have localised quicksands on either side of the water. If you encounter one, lie flat and move slowly out of the area.***

## Floating across

If the temperature of a body of water is warm enough for swimming but if you are unable to swim, make a flotation device to help you. Some things you can use are:

**1 Trousers**
Knot each leg at the bottom and button the fly. With both hands grasp the waistband at the sides and swing the trousers in the air to trap air in each leg. Quickly press the sides of the waistband together and hold it under water so that the air will not escape. You now have water wings to keep you afloat. These have to be re-inflated several times when crossing a wide stretch of water.

**2 Empty containers**
Lash together empty tins, petrol cans or boxes and use them as water wings. You should only use this type of flotation in a slow-moving river or stream.

**3 Plastic bags**
Air-fill two or more plastic bags and securely tie them together at the mouth.

**4 Poncho**
Roll green vegetation tightly inside your poncho so that you have a roll at least 45 cm in diameter. Tie the ends of the roll securely. You can wear it around your waist or across one shoulder and under the opposite arm.

**5 Logs**
Use a stranded drift log if one is available, or find a log near the water's edge. Test it before starting to cross, however, as some tree logs, palm for example, will sink even when the wood is dead.

**6 Bulrushes**
Gather stalks of bulrushes and tie them in a bundle 25 cm or more in diameter. The many air cells in each stalk cause it to float until it rots. Test the bundle to make sure it will support your weight before attempting to cross.

against can usually be crossed safely in this manner.

Do not rope your team together in fast-flowing water; the action of the current may hold any fallen member down.

## Flash floods

Beware rapidly-increased water flows. Flash floods are a common feature in the tropics, and can arrive suddenly many miles from any apparent storm. Try to cross steadily but quickly. Heat loss will be substantial, and you could quickly become weak. Once out on the other bank, take your clothes off and wring out as much water as possible. Change into dry kit if you can; otherwise, put your wet clothes back on – they'll soon dry out as your body warms up.

**ossing, with the current flowing at a 45° angle to the pole.**

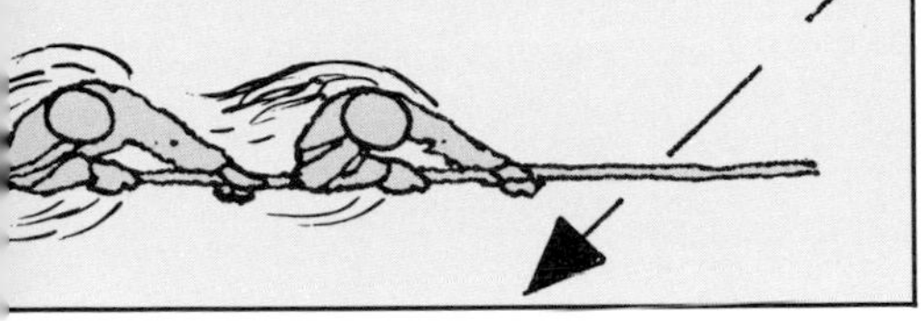

Avoid bubbly water under falls; it has little buoyancy.

### *Avoid cold water*

Be sure to check the water temperature before trying to cross a river or water obstacles. If the water is extremely cold and you are unable to find a shallow fording place, do not attempt to ford it. Devise other means for crossing; for instance, you might improvise a bridge by felling a tree over the river. Or you might build a raft large enough to carry both you and your equipment.

### *Other water obstacles*

You may also face bogs, quagmire, muskeg or quicksand. DO NOT try to walk across: trying to lift your feet while standing upright will make you sink deeper. If you are unable to bypass them, you may be able to bridge them using logs, branches or foliage.

Another way to cross is to lie face downwards with your arms spread and swim or pull your way across. Be sure to keep your body horizontal.

In swamps, the areas that have vegetation are usually firm enough to support your weight and you should be able to crawl or pull your way through miles of swamp or bog. In open mud or water areas without vegetation, you can swim.

## Log raft

This will carry both you and your equipment if you are unable to cross in any other way; if you have an axe and a knife you can build it without rope. A suitable raft for three men would be 12 ft long and 6 ft wide. You can use dry, dead, standing trees for logs, but spruce trees that are found in polar and sub-polar regions make the best log rafts.

**The only tools required are an axe and a knife**

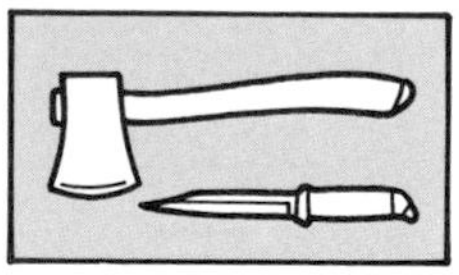

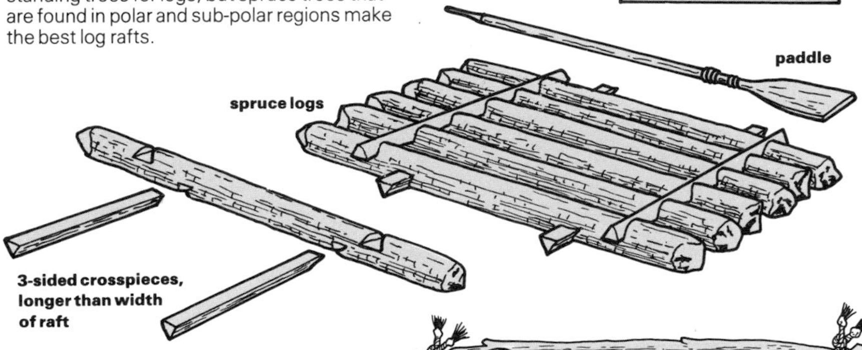

**1** Build the raft on two skid logs placed so that they slope downwards to the bank. Smooth the logs with an axe so that the raft logs lie evenly on them.
**2** Cut four offset inverted notches, one in the top and bottom of both ends of each log. Make the notches broader at the base than at the outer edge of the log.
**3** To bind the raft together, drive through each notch a three-sided wooden crosspiece about 30 cm longer than the width of the raft. Connect all the notches on one side of the raft before connecting those on the other.
**4** Lash the overhanging ends of the two crosspieces together at each end of the raft to give it additional strength. When the raft enters the water, the crosspieces swell, binding the logs together tightly.
**5** If the crosspieces fit too loosely, wedge them with thin pieces of dried wood. These swell when wet, tightening and strengthening the crosspieces.

### Crossing on a raft

A deep and fast-moving river can be crossed several times using a pendulum action at a bend in the river; this is necessary when several men have to cross. However, remember the following.

**1** The raft must be canted in the direction of the current.
**2** The rope from the anchor point must be 7-8 times as long as the width of the river.
**3** The attachment of the rope to the raft must be adjustable to change the cant of the raft so that it can return to the starting bank.

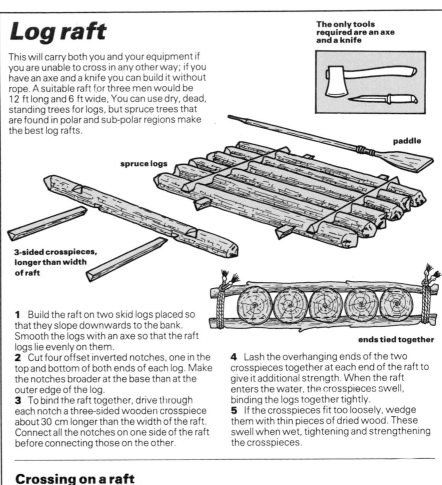

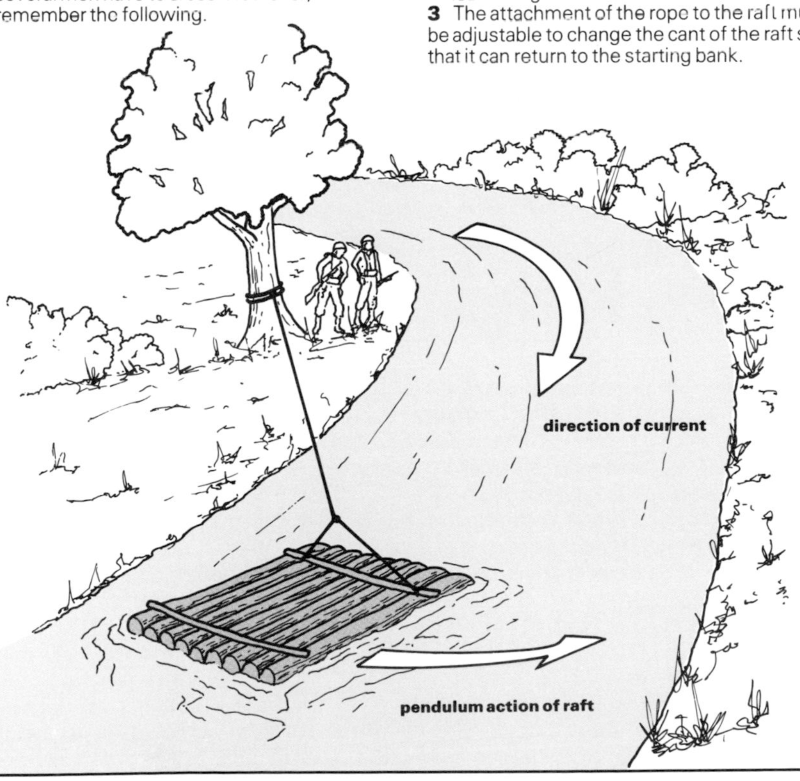

# GRABBING THE BASTARD TREE

***During a three-week ambush patrol, a platoon is usually choppered to a drop-off point about three days' march from the ambush area. On the route in, each section carries out its own patrol and will rendezvous at night at a platoon harbour location.*** Within a couple of kilometres of the objective, a local patrol will drop off to cover the ambush site while the platoon commander takes one of the sections and indicates an admin area. The section and platoon commanders then collect the section tasked with the ambush patrol and establish the ambush position. Once this has been done, the admin section commander will inform his men of the location.

Both sections are initially responsible for camp admin and the ambush patrol, rotating tasks every 24 hours. The third section, operating within three or four kilometres of the admin/ambush area, will spend a week on roving patrol before switching roles with one of the other sections.

Inter-patrol comms is maintained vocally by VHF, and the platoon linked to base by Morse Code on an HF net. Normal radio procedure is permitted for just one hour at a given time in the morning, and again in the evening 12 hours later. A 24-hour listening watch is also maintained and the base guard platoon has a standby section and chopper on permanent call – just in case! It is reassuring to know that you are not entirely on your own.

## Ambush patrols

Your section is on its fourth day in ambush. When you arrived in Belize several months ago all of this was

The long-term ambush is a real test of endurance even in the best English summer: in Belize it is hell. However, the proximity of the Guatemalan border and armed drug smugglers mean that there is plenty of incentive to treat this as more than just an exercise.

*These are captured marijuana growers. Faced with the option of growing a staple food crop or drugs, peasant farmers will choose drugs: they can then afford to buy more food than they could grow.*

totally new. Now you're quite used to the routine. Having sweated through the dry season, you feel like a seasoned veteran. This is your last jungle trip, and then it's back to England – not before time, you think, as it begins to rain. Hard to decide which is worse – the dry season with its interminable heat, or the rainy season with its torrential downpours!

You slightly shift position for the hundredth time and scan the track, just visible below and to your front. Nothing. You glance at your mate crouched on your left. He is drenched, rivulets of rainwater running through his matted hair and trickling from his chin. His blank expression is typical of everyone's in the section.

## Pissing it down

At last the rain begins to peter out. It's always the same. Three or four hours of pissing it down in the morning, before settling off for the afternoon. After the rain comes the humidity – the mist and the heat, lasting until about 1700 hours, when it again chucks it down until around 2200. The rain causes rivers to swell and burst their banks, and quickly turns low ground into mangrove swamp.

It also brings out some horrible bugs. You shudder as you think about the luminous flying *things* known as 'basha beetles'. At night, these black, inch-long creatures scurry beneath bashas to shelter from the rain. In the morning it isn't unusual to find the roof of your poncho swarming with them!

And when you are so close to Guatemala, there's a risk of being ambushed by the drug smugglers. To counter the threat, you operate a 'hard routine', which means no hot meals, cigarettes or even a brew! There's no talking – just hand signals, and at night you're not allowed the luxury of a poncho, so even the bloody 'basha beetles' leave you alone. You just loosen the straps of your Bergen, and each four-man patrol goes to sleep sitting back to back. Thank goodness it isn't like this all the time!

*Patrolling is all about gathering information. Here a member of the Belize Defence Force and the patrol commander chat to a rubber tapper during a local mobile patrol.*

The problem with these Mexican drug smugglers caught on the border was that they had had time to stash all signs of the true nature of their business, and had to be released for lack of evidence.

This river marks the crossing point between Belize and Guatemala. The foliage gives some idea of the density of the jungle and the problems in hunting down small bands of heavily-armed drug smugglers with a great deal to gain and virtually nothing to lose.

Still, you've learned a lot from being out here. It might not have been all pleasant, but it's been good experience. What about the time when you had to rope in from a chopper, down through the canopy into a mangrove swamp? You spent two weeks up to your waist in water, and at night you had to erect your hammock in the trees!

Or how about when you were operating down south? Until then, you never really believed that there were baboons in this part of the world. But there they were! To prevent the bastards from running off with your kit you were forced to wrap your Bergen inside a poncho and suspend it from a tree close to your head as you lay in your hammock.

You soon learned what insects to look out for, and what plants to avoid. There's a particularly nasty specimen covered with two-inch-long thorns. When anyone grabbed hold of it he often screamed 'Bastard!' so it inevitably became known as the 'Bastard Tree'!

Of course, you've also learned some practical things. The locals showed you how to obtain water from a plant known as the water vine. You just cut yourself a metre-long section, lopped off the bottom, followed by the top, and the water trickled out – only enough to fill an eggcup, but water nonetheless. Out here, knowing that could save your life!

Below: A drug smugglers' airstrip. The profits from smuggling are so vast that there is little the drug smuggler cannot achieve. Belize is one area where the Army have a very worthwhile and difficult job to do.

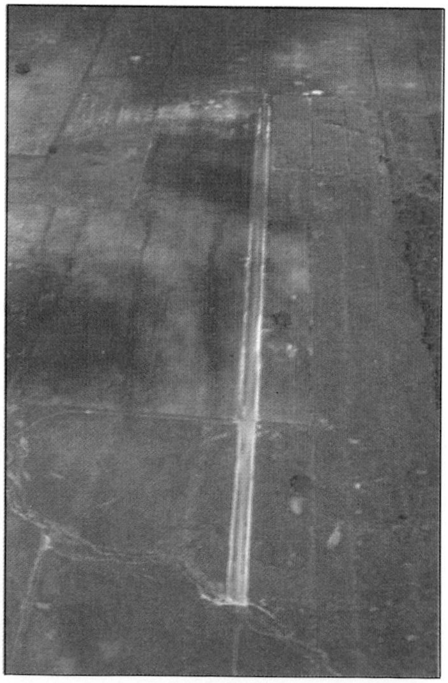

### Down to the NAAFI

A cold beer would certainly save your life right now, you think. Still, there'll be time for a few of those once you're out of the jungle. You'll get off the chopper, head straight for the block, clean your weapon and hand it in to the armoury. Then it'll be down to the NAAFI for a crate of 'Schlitz'. Afterwards you'll have a nice, long shower and a shave before changing into clean shorts, T-shirt and flip-flops and heading back to the NAAFI.

Half of your six weeks 'off' will be spent on camp guard duty. The other half will be taken up by platoon and adventure training, ambush exercises and local patrols. It's not so bad when you have the NAAFI to sustain you, and when that gets boring there's always the nearby town's rum shack with its locally brewed charcoal rum (and coke). Just another six weeks to do – then it'll be back to England.

In the meantime, though, there's a job to do, so you just have to crack on with it. You'll continue to lie here until the ambush comes off or until you are relieved. Anyone observed on the track will be stopped and questioned – what possible reason would they have for crossing the border here? There's no village close by, nothing, in fact, except a marijuana field off the track further along.

A big raindrop lands on the wet leaves in front of your face. Here we go again. You glance at the time – just after five o'clock. You can almost set your watch by it. Oh, well, not long to do now . . .

# Combat Report

## Vietnam: Riverine Patrol Part 2

The VC were incredibly cunning at hiding weapons and supplies aboard river craft. We had to check out everything that floated because they often tried to smuggle things right under our noses.

**Don Montgomery continues his story of a riverine patrol in the Mekong Delta during the Vietnam War, in February 1966.**

We had our guns reloaded and started back in toward the beach and all those VC guns. Charlie started hitting us harder than ever. Bullets were sailing through the hull and bouncing off the armour plate. Luck had been with us so far, but we could not count on it lasting for ever. Shortage of ammo or not, we were forced to lay down a heavy barrage of automatic fire.

Jump yelled at me to spray the treetops. I brought the .50s up, and coconuts and palm branches flew into the air – then a body dropped from the trees. The incoming fire momentarily stopped.

### The .50s rattled and shook

The Skyraiders had expended all their bombs and were now strafing the beaches. Andy 88, the Forward Air Controller, came on the radio and advised that he was overhead and that three F-100 Super Sabres were on their way from Saigon. The Skyraiders made one last pass over the beaches, looped over the target area and flew off. Andy 88 advised that the jets would be along in about five minutes.

The firing picked up the moment the Skyraiders left, and as we approached the western end of the grove several VC ran on to the beach and headed for a large junk partially hidden in undergrowth at the water's edge. We turned all the guns on it; I hit the lead man and he was knocked to the ground.

The aft .50 and .30 cal machine-guns dealt with the rest of the VC soldiers, and I turned my .50s to the junk itself. I could see two gun barrels pointing out of the portholes to the rear of the wheelhouse; a Browning automatic rifle started firing from one of them. The bullets struck the water and were walking out towards us, but stopped – the clip had run out.

He started a second clip at the same point and attempted to walk it in, and once again he emptied the mag before reaching our boat. Before he learned to correct his fire, I pushed down on the trigger bar and started walking my fire in. The sixth or seventh round caught the bow square on and I continued to fire without letting up.

The .50s rattled and shook; the smell of burning powder grew strong in the air. Large chunks of the hull were blown away and finally the incendiary ammo set light to the fuel. The old oil in the bilges caught, and thick black smoke filled the sky. The smell of burning powder grew strong in the air. Large chunks of the hull were blown away, and finally the junk was enveloped in flames.

We again withdrew to mid-river to re-arm the guns. The Super Sabres were rolling in now, and we stayed out in the river as they bombed and strafed for the next half hour. As they reformed to return to Saigon they told us they would get more bombs and return.

Several machine-gun emplacements had survived the bombing, and as soon as the jet left we were again under heavy automatic fire. We also took rifle fire from the centre of the grove.

Benny yelled to hit the tree tops with M-79 grenades; Sweatman opened up with the belt-fed launcher and the rifle fire suddenly stopped. For over 2½ hours we fought their emplacements in the hot afternoon sun. Every time we saw a sampan or junk hidden in the underbush, we would shoot up the hull so they could not use it to escape down-river or attack us mid-stream.

### The 142 approaches

We were running very low on ammo now. Jump called on the radio for the outcoming patrol's location. They were only a little over half way to our position, and one of the boats was experiencing bilge pump difficulty and was taking on enough water to slow it down. The other boat took some of its ammo and continued at high speed to our assistance.

It was 15 minutes before we spotted the approaching boat: John Gilman's PBR 142. By now I was using my old 'Tommy' gun, Benny was firing an AK-47 and John Sweatman was using a ChiCom that had been converted to take .308 ammo.

### A steak dinner

The 142 came alongside and started passing ammo over to us and we re-armed the .50s. When all three boats were ready we moved in to make the kill. As we were closing the beach, Andy 88 advised that the Super Sabres were back again, and the VC found themselves confronted from the sea and air at the same time.

The jets roared in to drop their deadly payloads, and we were close enough to call the locations of the gun emplacements and close enough to hit the buildings in the jungle. We hit six of them and got secondary explosions from four. We then made a slow run along the beach, continuously levelling concentrated fire into the enemy positions while the jets strafed the grove with 20-mm cannon fire.

We finally headed home at 16.00 hours, passing the 139 boat en route. Their bilge pump was now repaired and they were heading down to join 142, unhappy at having missed the fight.

We docked, and to our surprise we were taken up to a hotel for a steak dinner the CO had gotten fixed for us. It had been quite a day. Two weeks later an intelligence report came in from Saigon informing us that a document had been captured by a SEAL team operating in Go Cong province, stating that the Viet Cong lost 54 killed in action and 27 wounded in the battle at the coconut grove.

**The end of another patrol. We later found that the VC had suffered over 80 casualties during the battle at Coconut Grove.**

# GALLANT EAGLE

*Joint operations between British and other NATO units can be a fascinating business. Here soldiers of the Parachute Regiment jump from American C-141 StarLifters into an exercise in the Californian Mojave desert.*

***Paratroopers must be able to operate in every kind of climate and all types of terrain: from the steaming jungles of Belize, to the gloomy backstreets of Belfast; from the frozen mountains of Norway in winter, to the parched landscape of the Middle East.***

Desert warfare exercises are often conducted in Oman – but not always. Exercise Gallant Eagle, for instance, presents some of you with an opportunity of visiting the United States, where you will operate alongside American troops in a massive airborne exercise, scheduled to take place in California's Mojave Desert.

After arriving at Pope Air Force Base (Fort Bragg), you get time to acclimatise, but during this time there is plenty to do: cross-training lets you and your American allies try out one another's personal weapons. For the Americans, this is their first opportunity to handle the SA80. Most are instantly won over by the British weapon, preferring it to their own Armalites!

## Swapping skills

The Patrols Platoon is paired off with its American counterpart – the Scout Platoon – and both make the most of this chance to swap ideas and compare skills. The British paras also take the opportunity to become proficient in operating American radios.

Because you will be jumping from

*Helicopter support is on a scale undreamt of in the British army. 'C' Company is deployed forward from the Drop Zone by US Army Black Hawk helicopters.*

American aircraft, using American parachutes and equipment, everyone has to be trained in local procedure. Both US and British troops must be able to work in conjunction, so it is essential to co-ordinate your own rallying drills with American tactics. As it is 82nd Airborne policy to drop at night, this takes some practice.

Another factor to consider is that American paratroopers are trained to deploy from the gigantic C-141 StarLifter – a *jet* aircraft! It is a totally new experience for you. With the familiar C-130 'Herc', you have to throw yourself out through the door to clear the sill. Not so in a C-141. As you reach the exit, the slipstream *sucks* you out – an alarming experience!

***You wait to board the giant C-141 StarLifter. You have to learn how to use American kit and fit in with their standard operational procedures. This means a night drop from a jet aircraft: a far cry from the familiar C-130 Hercules.***

## Early drop

After two and a half weeks you are ready to start the exercise, with the drop scheduled to take place in the early hours of the morning. Men, tanks and other vehicles are to be deployed from 48 StarLifters in a single pass over two parallel DZs! During the exercise, your company will be attached to 3rd Battalion, the 504th Parachute Infantry Regiment.

At last it's time to emplane. Your aircraft is just one in a long line of C-141s. As you file aboard, the howl of jet engines fills the night in a deafening crescendo. Parachutes are loaded separately, to be fitted during the flight out – something else that takes some getting used to. When you taxi onto the runway, it seems as though there is hardly any space between the aircraft as each machine takes off close behind the other.

***Before the exercise starts you have two weeks to master US parachutes, radios, rallying drills and all the minutiae of airborne operations. Your hosts are 3/504th Infantry Regiment, part of the famous 82nd Airborne Division.***

## Fitting 'chutes

Parachutes are distributed when you are three and a half hours into the flight. With 100 men in each aircraft, it's quite a struggle to fit 'chutes. Despite the C-141's highly efficient air-conditioning, you are soon pouring with sweat, and it is another hour and a half before everyone is finally settled.

The troop transports are now joined by the tank and vehicle carriers. As the StarLifters close up, the wash from the lead aircraft causes your own to tremble and rock.

At 03.00 you finally stand and hook up. Red on . . . Green . . . GO! You're

***The ground is rock hard – indeed, it consists of little else but rocks. Digging in is impossible, so you build sangers. This para is on stag, part of a defensive position blocking a pass through the hills.***

sucked into space and, after your 'chute snaps open, there is an unforgettable sight. The beautiful, clear, moonlit sky is filled with thousands of parachutes. They drift gently down, to land among countless vehicles dropped moments before and now covering the DZ.

On the ground, you hurriedly RV with the rest of the company. There are only two injuries. Not bad at all. In less than 30 minutes you are on the move. While the division concentrates on securing and clearing the area in preparation for a second drop, your company is held in reserve before being choppered forward to block likely enemy approach routes. The rocky terrain of the Black Mountains makes digging in virtually impossible. Instead, you construct stone sangers, camouflaging your efforts with desert tumbleweed.

### Without water

With the intense heat of the rising sun, water resupply now becomes something of a priority. Dehydration is a serious danger. Those in Patrols Platoon – without water for 72 hours – become desperate, and are forced to drink the fluid from medical saline drips! When you are finally resupplied nobody can believe their eyes. Besides 1,000-gal water containers, the Americans bring forward huge freezer wagons full of ice and chocolate milk!

Fortified, you settle in to wait for the start of the Big Push. When it begins, the horizon is filled with huge dust clouds thrown up by the tracks of 'enemy' armour. As the tanks approach the pass, it becomes evident that your minefields and anti-tank ditches are going to force the enemy into a bottleneck – and a carefully sited killing area!

The division itself is not even put under pressure, and much to the disappointment of the Americans, the British paras get all the action. In a decisive battle the 'enemy' is forced to pull back and bug out. Victory!

Feeling decidedly chuffed, you withdraw and regroup at the airhead, where you refit in preparation for a daylight drop back into Fort Bragg.

When you jump in, you are amazed to be greeted by a vast crowd of onlookers. Brass bands and applauding families herald your arrival, and dozens of film crews record the occasion. Salisbury Plain was never like this! None of you have ever known anything like it: air-conditioned aircraft ... iced milk chocolate in the field ... and now a heroes' welcome for those returning from exercise. What an experience – a great way to earn your American wings!

***Ready for the drop. It is the 82nd Airborne's policy to make all tactical drops at night. On this exercise, 48 of the monstrous jets will each drop 100 men during a single pass over two parallel drop zones.***

***Catching some rays at Endex. The resupply included chocolate milk and ice cream, which was an interesting change from British Army scoff. Even more surprising was returning to Fort Bragg to find bands playing and crowds cheering!***